THE
COMMUNICAT
TOOLKIT

THE COMMUNICATION TOOLKIT

Assessing and Developing Social Communication Skills in Children and Adolescents

BELINDA MEDHURST

Illustrated by Nicky Armstrong

HINTON HOUSE

Published by
Hinton House Publishers Ltd, Newman House, 4 High Street, Buckingham,
MK18 1NT, UK
info@hintonpublishers.com

www.hintonpublishers.com

First published 2009
Reprinted 2010, 2012, 2013, 2015

Printed and bound in the United Kingdom by Hobbs the Printers Ltd

British Library Cataloguing in Publication Data

Medhurst, Belinda.
   The communication toolkit : assessing & developing social communication
   skills in children and adolescents.
   1. Communicative disorders in children. 2. Social skills in children. 3. Social
   skills in children--Study and teaching. 4. Developmentally disabled children--
   Education. 5. Developmentally disabled--Means of communication.
   I. Title
   371.9'0446-dc22

ISBN 978 1 906531 26 3

FSC
www.fsc.org
MIX
Paper from
responsible sources
FSC® C020438

Contents

Worksheets

About the author

Belinda Medhurst is a Chartered Educational Psychologist (BSc, PGCE, MEd, CPsychol) and is a member of the Division of Education and Child Psychology (British Psychological Society). She qualified as a Psychologist in 1991 and as a Teacher in 1993.

Belinda has worked as an Educational Psychologist for local authorities since qualifying, including eight years for Hampshire County Council. During this time she occupied the role as Senior Specialist Educational Psychologist for Autism and Language Impairment. This role involved setting up of specialist units of provision for Autistm Spectrum Disordered youngsters, together with the development and coordination of county-wide support programmes including TOP – Thomas Outreach Project and SLIP – Secondary Language Impairment Project.

She has a passion for supporting children with a wide range of needs, applying a practical approach which is well grounded in theoretical perspective. Belinda believes strongly in supporting the whole child through an eclectic range of tools, tailored to the individual needs of each youngster. Currently, she practices independently in Hampshire.

Introduction

What is *The Communication Toolkit*?

This resource pack is designed to support communication skills in children and young people aged 8 to16 who experience challenges in social situations. It will also provide valuable insight for professionals working with young people on their perspectives of themselves, others and the world around them.

These youngsters will be considered to have symptoms of an autism spectrum disorder (ASD), though not always a diagnosis.

These symptoms will usually include:
- An inability to see their own behaviour as unacceptable or unusual;
- Poor self-concept and self-esteem;
- Problems in group situations and class but 'acceptable' behaviour one to one.

There is an acknowledged increase in the numbers of children and young people being diagnosed with an ASD. Some may have 'features' of an ASD or are described as not experiencing a full range of typical ASD symptoms. For instance, they may demonstrate some empathy or understanding of others' situations. Commonly, these children may be described as experiencing 'Asperger's Syndrome', and may have difficulties that are similar to those experienced by children on the 'mild' end of the autism spectrum.

These young people may not always respond to the interventions classically applied in supporting ASD children, such as Visual Timetables, Social Skills Groups or Social Stories. Such youngsters may have some insight into their behaviours and experience some degree of distance from their peers. These children may:
- Appear aloof or distant from peers.
- Find friendships difficult to develop or maintain.
- Become confused, frustrated or anxious in social situations.

- Present as unpredictable and moody.
- Demonstrate behavioural challenges.
- Misunderstand social applications of language.
- Present unusual patterns of behaviour and communication style.

For these young people, a more detailed and personal perspective may be more helpful, which develops their understanding of themselves and the world around them. It may be that issues of attachment, family, friendship and self-esteem have resulted in poor social behaviour and understanding. Quite often these difficulties are compounded by the onset of puberty, which places huge social pressure on youngsters with weaknesses in social skills. Tutoring these youngsters on self and social understanding will help them to be more likely to engage with self- and social knowledge. As a result they will have more successful interactions and relationships.

The Communication Toolkit draws on a variety of theoretical backgrounds including emotional literacy, self-concept, solution-focused and social-use-of-language approaches.

This resource is divided into four sections that will:
- Identify personal qualities and experiences in the context of the wider world.
- Allow young people to tell their own story.
- Develop social and emotional awareness and understanding.
- Develop survival strategies that promote positive behaviour and improved communication.

These are intended, through specific and structured photocopiable activities to develop emotional literacy, self-esteem, social understanding and ultimately, behaviour and communication in those in the 8 to16 age range. This is particularly useful for both middle and secondary school transitions, often a turbulent time for those with an emotional or communication difficulty.

Why *The Communication Toolkit*?

Young people with communication and social understanding difficulties need specific tuition on aspects of self- and social identity. They also need to have interactions and communication broken down and interpreted for them in a more simple way. This enables them to create their own social understanding and appropriate responses. Such a programme needs to be individualised for each child and related to the specific weaknesses and strengths that they bring to social situations.

By breaking down their social understanding into its component parts the youngster will be more able to make sense of situations and adjust their behaviours. This process starts with understanding themselves, then understanding others, and finally, understanding themselves and others together. This is what *The Communication Toolkit* aims to achieve.

Who should use *The Communication Toolkit*?

The Communication Toolkit is both a resource and an assessment tool, as it develops understanding of the child, and allows the professionals working with them to review specific difficulties and explore individual needs. For this reason many different practitioners, including speech and language therapists, psychologists and teachers, will find this resource invaluable.

How does *The Communication Toolkit* work?

The Communication Toolkit allows the professional working with a young person to follow a process of self-discovery before social discovery. The young person needs to have a good sense of self-identity and the first section, 'Who Am I?', thoroughly researches 'self-concept' through a variety of getting-to-know-me activities. This will help gain a knowledge of the young person's level of self-esteem, view of their families and friends and who they are as individuals. For many youngsters this is a evolving subject which they may need to revisit in the future.

The next section, 'About Other People', reviews how the young person sees others in society, and begins to reveal how they see the world around them. This section is important as it will help professionals gain an understanding of how the young person views conversations, social groups and other people's behaviour.

This follows naturally on to looking at behaviour in social contexts, and viewing strengths and weaknesses, 'About Me with Others'. It helps to illustrate to the young person where they may be going wrong in social contexts, and identify some important social strengths.

Finally, 'Developing Skills' pulls together ideas for developing an individualised programme of support, based on improved self- and social knowledge. By this stage the young person should be more aware of their individual strengths but also the social errors they are making. The activities are designed to empower, encourage and develop an effective set of tools for social growth and competency. It is not a 'quick fix' solution in itself and the interventions and management strategies can only usefully be applied when the individual has developed the skills covered in previous sections.

It is not necessary to cover of all the sections in sequence, or even all the contents of a section. This resource allows the professional to tailor a set of activities and interventions to meet the individual's specific needs.

How is *The Communication Toolkit* organised?

The contents of this resource are summarised below:

1. **Who Am I?** Activities around self-concept, memories, friendships, 'what do others value in me' are discussed and a historic and current 'album' can be created from the information gathered.

2. **About Other People** Practical sessions on greetings, social-reasoning, social prediction and understanding how to correct social mistakes, turn-taking and developing trust.

3. **About Me with Others** The interaction of the individual and their social groups, including family and friends. A review of communication skills in all settings.

4. **Developing Skills** Including self-esteem boosters, managing emotions and how to promote positive language skills socially. Also social skills exercises, practical targets, rewards and 'what next' ideas.

What tools does *The Communication Toolkit* use?

The activities and resources are photocopiable and many are illustrated with cartoons that will encourage interaction between the adult and young person. Completed worksheets from the resource can be used by professionals in schools and elsewhere to create the young person's own file or 'album' and allow their story to be told.

Worksheet activities include:

- Photographs of family and friends
- Diagrams to complete (e.g., family trees, life-maps)
- Pictures of incidents, situations, people and life events
- Cartoon strips to describe situations
- Rating-scale activities (e.g., 'agree or disagree' statements)
- Word-circle and sentence completion activities
- Social-situation activities (using pictures and cartoons)
- Picture scanning opportunities.

The worksheets are clearly presented to enable easy selection of the activity most appropriate for the young person.

If the young person you are working with has poor reading skills, read the worksheet with them and ensure they understand the instructions before commencing the activity. Equally, if handwriting skills are an issue worksheets can be enlarged or answers written or drawn on separate sheets.

Each section in the *Toolkit* is preceded by explanatory notes that correspond to the practical activities. These notes are boxed to differentiate them from the worksheets and will allow the professional to understand the rationale behind each activity and how to gather and use the information to best effect.

Section 1
Who Am I?

This section will help you gain a range of information about the young person you are working with. This includes their views of themselves as an individual (self-concept) and also what they value in themselves (self-esteem).

By working through this section you should gain a clearer understanding of the internal conflicts, confusion and self-esteem issues faced by the young person and some knowledge of the type of activities which help them make progress.

Who am I?

You are going to work on how you feel about yourself. These activities will help you to look at yourself in detail and find out more about who you are!

Topics will cover:

- What do you think about yourself?
- How do you feel in different places and with different people?
- How do you behave in different places and with different people?
- What do you enjoy and what are you good at?
- What are your interests?

You will need to:

- Look closer at who you are

    - Ask questions

    - Be honest and truthful

- Draw, talk about and write some answers.

Let's get started!

My family

The activities in this section will allow you to explore safely a variety of issues relating to home life with young people.

If you have concerns about family relationships or wish to develop trust in working with a young person these are good activities to start with. It is important to remember when working on 'My Family' that some youngsters may be confused about who is in their 'family' and this activity can help to highlight any misconceptions.

The first activity is a drawing of the family group with the individual positioned within it. Look for:

- Who is dominant in the picture?
- Is the child in the middle / at the edge / shown as large or small – do they look insignificant or part of the group?
- Do the family members look happy?
- Which clothes are worn and why?
- Are some family members excluded and if so, why?
- Are some people not really 'family' and if so, why are they included?

Discuss the following after completion of the activity.

- Is the child keen to talk about their family?
- Who do they talk about the most?
- Who do they avoid talking about? Why is this?
- Are there people missing from their picture? Why?

My family

Who is in your family? Make a list here:

- _____
- _____
- _____
- _____

Draw a picture of your family in the box below and remember to include yourself.

What are you all doing, and where are you?

Think about the clothes people might be wearing.

If you like, you can also add a photograph of your family, or a person in your family who is important to you.

Who do I feel closest to in my family?

This activity explores how the young person feels about different people in their family, using a representation of the family group. Positioning themselves closer to or more distant from someone can indicate how close the young person feels to that person.

When the child has finished labelling the cartoon explore with them:

- Who is closest to them and why?
- Who is furthest away and why?
- Are there absent family members, if so, why?
- Are there any positions they would like to change on reflection?
- Who do they share similar thoughts or feelings with?

Try to encourage the young person to talk about memories relating to why they may have positioned a family member in a particular position. If there have been splits in the family this exercise is helpful in identifying how the child may feel about these.

Some young people might be members of several families and complex relationships may have formed. Explore how they feel about this and if necessary more discussion may be needed around issues such as feelings of anger or resentment, legitimacy of family membership and who is a 'real' brother or sister.

Who do I feel closest to in my family?

Sometimes there are people in your family you feel closer to than others. These might be the family members you spend most time with or they might be the people you most like talking to or being with.

Take a few minutes to think about who you feel close to and why, and then write names on the people in the picture, with the person you feel closest to next to you, and the person you feel least close to furthest away.

You can draw more people if you need to.

Me

What my family think of me

This is an ideal activity to develop a young person's understanding of how they are viewed by other members of their family. You may find that they need to be questioned or challenged to elicit valid views that are not based on skewed perceptions (e.g., 'Are you really sure your mum thinks you are horrible/angelic?').

Be sure to check:

- Whose perspective is being explored and why?
- Is the child really sure a person thinks such things about them?
- Are there any other words that might apply?
- Are there any other words not on the page they want to use?
- Is there a need to encourage more circling of words?
- Is there a focus on negative or positive qualities?

Note how many negative qualities have been used and whether you feel the young person displays low self-esteem.

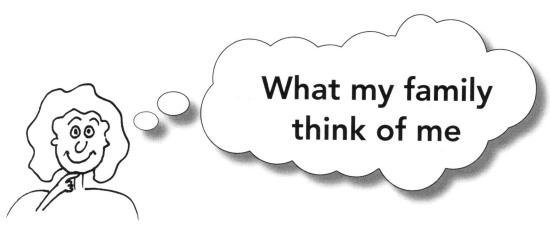

What my family think of me

This activity will help you try to see yourself from your family's point of view – what does your family think about you?

Choose one pen colour for family members who know you well, and circle the words that describe how they might think of you.

Now choose another pen colour for people who don't know you very well and circle the words that describe how they might think of you.

honest   shy   kind

giggly   fun   naughty   bubbly

unhappy   QUIET

unkind

LOUD   helpful

nasty

energetic   selfish

MOODY

happy   aggressive

Where am I from?

This activity is very useful for young people who are confused about their family group and relationships.

If a family has split up, or has experienced re-marriage or adoptions, it is important that the young person has a clear idea of how people are related to them within their extended family group. This may uncover some sensitive issues, where anger, resentment, confusion and denial may be apparent. The previous exercises should give an indication of whether the child might be uncomfortable discussing these issues.

Note: This activity should be avoided if you feel the child is not yet ready to explore these relationships. Similarly, some parents may feel uncomfortable with professionals exploring this subject if there are unresolved issues.

Points to consider:

- Is the child clear about who occupies which role?
- Are there issues not known to the child?
- How does the child feel about the members of their extended family?
- Does the child understand the 'growth' nature of the tree and that it will change?
- Is the child keen to follow up on some of the research for this?
- How can you support the child to complete follow-up work?

It is important to ensure that this activity ends with the young person feeling positive and reassured.

Where am I from?

You are going to draw your family tree.

Do you know the names and birth dates of your parents, grandparents, aunts and uncles or carers?

Do you have any step-parents or half brothers or sisters?

Think about your family group and add some names to the family tree on the next sheet. If you know other details such as dates of birth you could add those too.

If there are people in your family whose names you don't know, or if you have questions about them perhaps there is someone who can help you find the answers.

You may need to take this worksheet home with you so you can fill in the gaps with help from your family.

MY FAMILY

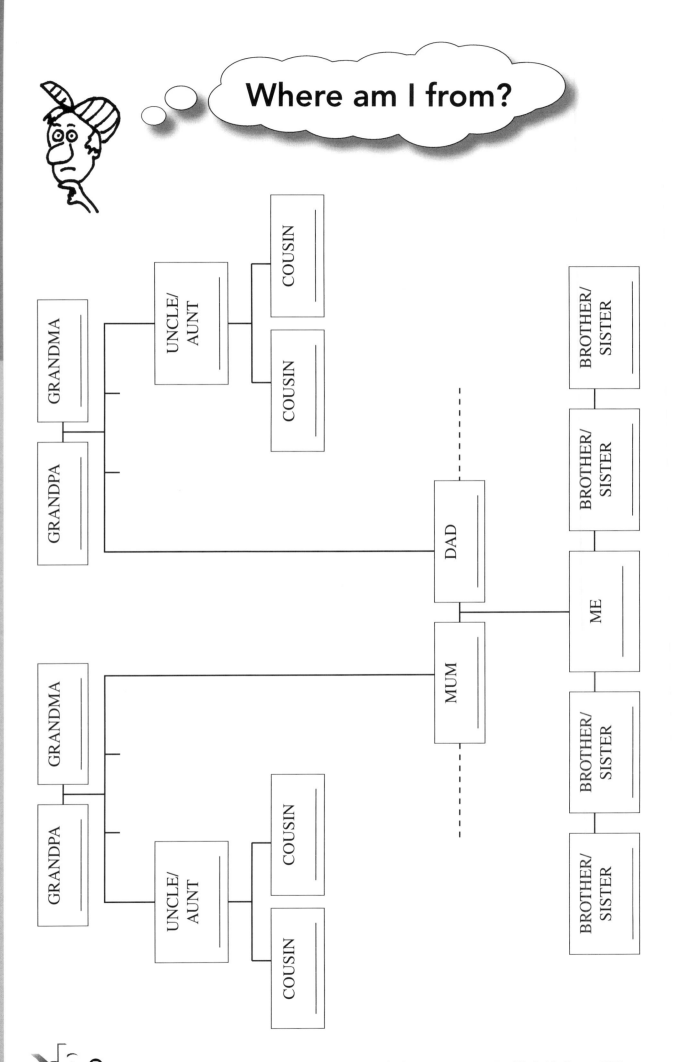

Where am I from?

GRANDMA

GRANDPA

UNCLE/
AUNT

COUSIN

COUSIN

DAD

GRANDMA

GRANDPA

UNCLE/
AUNT

COUSIN

COUSIN

MUM

ME

BROTHER/
SISTER

BROTHER/
SISTER

BROTHER/
SISTER

BROTHER/
SISTER

BROTHER/
SISTER

Memories

The activities in this section develop further ideas of family, and explore some of the important memories that have helped to shape the young person's understanding of their emotional world.

Some activities in this section may be difficult for the young person to complete, as they naturally forget, or even wilfully repress, memories. It is important to uncover the readily available memories in the first instance, and then allow them to go away and develop their own recollections further in private if necessary.

Many youngsters with an ASD will have problems in recalling emotional content of memories. This can be developed through exploring their physical feelings at the time of the event.

Photograph album

This is good starting point for building up memories through the use of visual cues and pictures.

It is also a good activity for the young person to start with an adult and then to develop further independently. They could be encouraged to work together with family members on researching and discussing photographs of key events. Encourage the young person to create their own photograph album to help learn more about their past memories - ensure they leave space to add photographs of new events. This will also help to develop the concept of time and events yet to happen.

Issues to consider:

- Be aware that in some families photographs are rarely taken, or that the family may be so dispersed that photographs are not available; try to work around this creatively, perhaps by asking the child to draw each person as part of a 'portrait gallery'.
- Some families can be reluctant to give precious photographs to children – they could be lent for a short time and photocopied for this exercise.
- Ensure that the child feels safe while looking at and talking through photographs and memories. This activity can sometimes evoke powerful emotions such as anger and rage. Alternatively, you may find it releases no emotions at all, leaving the child with little to discuss at this stage.

Photograph album

Here is a chance to collect together some photographs of important people or events in your life. You can add some extra sheets if you need to.

If you haven't got photographs, you can write a description or draw a picture of what happened instead.

Here are some examples of photographs you may like to use:

- My earliest birthday party
- My favourite holiday
- My favourite Christmas
- My favourite family gathering
- Photograph of my friends
- A photograph of my pet
- A family photograph I really like

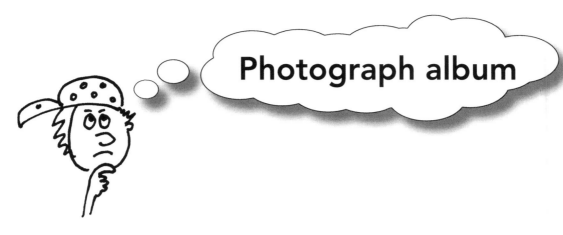

Photograph album

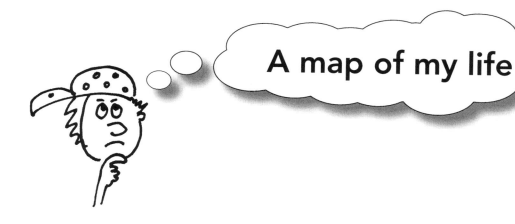

A map of my life

This is an important activity that encourages the young person to list chronologically key events of their life.

Points to note:

- Ensure the child lists events that they feel are important.
- Moving house may be seen as unimportant, but attending a first football match essential.
- Try to get a balance of positive and negative events (i.e., not just celebrations).
- If the young person has difficulty remembering events, use key dates as prompts (e.g., birthdays, school changes, house moves, births and deaths, holidays).
- The child may wish to use key words to represent a memory – ensure you both understand what these mean and record them if necessary.
- Explore the events as far as the young person feels comfortable.
- Try to elicit emotional reactions to the events ('How did that make you *feel*?')
- Use physical reactions to gauge emotional ones if the child is having difficulty remembering feelings.
- Don't be afraid of moving further along the time line, and revisiting an uneventful period later.

Extension Activity
- If the child wishes, another sheet of paper can be added to the top of the 'map'. This can be used to explore where they are about to go, or where they want to go.

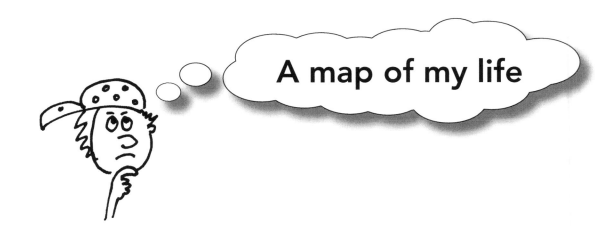

A map of my life

Life can be seen as being like a journey – the road can be straight forward, or bumpy, or with lots of bends and twists.

On the map, fill in important events that have happened in your life on the signposts and places along the road. You can write these ('Moved house') or draw them (a picture of the new house), whichever you prefer.

Some Ideas

- You may wish to put good things on the left and bad things on the right.
- You could use a different colour pen for good events and bad events.
- Try to write down equal numbers of good and bad events.

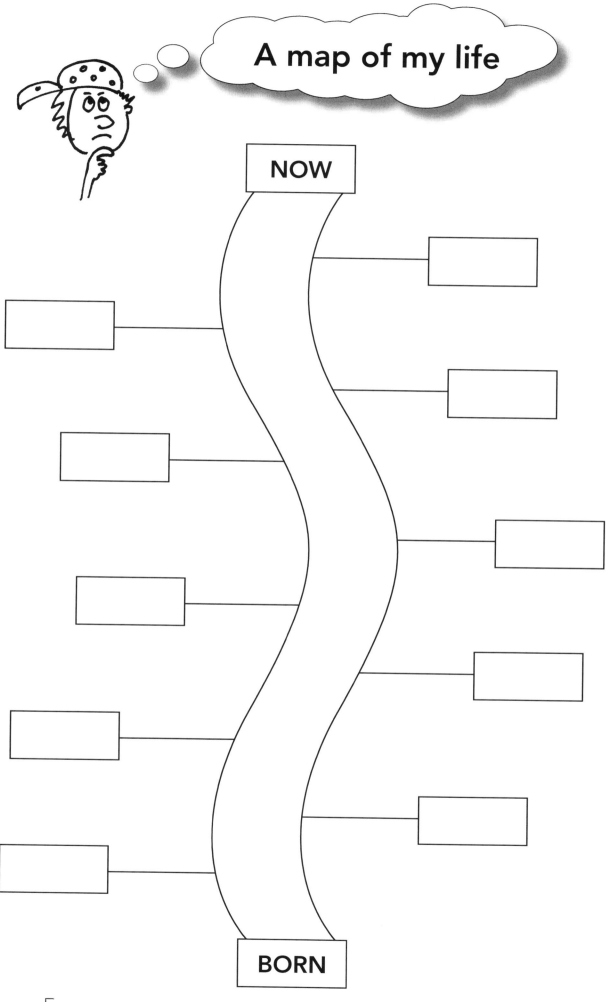

A map of my life

NOW

BORN

Events and sensations

This activity is good for young people with episodic memory difficulties – those who can record memories factually, but without emotional understanding or recognition. Some children will find this exercise difficult and you will need to use careful questions to break down some of their memories with them.

- Do they remember any physical sensations that accompanied the event? These can often be a clue to emotional reactions to a situation and can help identify feelings.

- Did they have particular thoughts about the situation? Sometimes they may have been confused, and children can often remember thoughts with more ease than feelings.

Try to obtain as much information as possible about the event and record it in a form that is accessible to the young person. Some children may prefer to draw a cartoon for example, with speech and thought bubbles to illustrate expressions. Others may like to use cuttings from magazines. You could use a large sheet of paper to extend the activity if necessary and keep it on a wall where the child can visit it and add memories as they remember them.

Events and sensations

When you remember events in your life, do you remember the feelings or physical sensations that you had at the time? Sometimes we can remember these feelings and sensations very clearly.

Take a few minutes to think back on some events which you remember clearly. What did you feel at the time?

Here is an example with the remembered feelings and sensations underlined:

'Paul went to the cinema for the first time when he was six years old. He remembers lots of people and hushed voices. Then it went dark and Paul couldn't see very well. He remembers a <u>tingling sensation</u> down his back as the sound of the film started. Paul's <u>heart started to beat really fast and hard</u>, as if it was getting bigger in his chest. When Paul looked up a big, bright light flashed onto the screen and he had to close his eyes because <u>it hurt to look at the light</u>.'

Think of something that has happened to you and try to remember your physical sensations at the time. Write the event in the box below, and circle some sensations from the list or think of your own. Next, try to remember any thoughts you had at the time. What did you want to happen next?

Event	Physical Sensation	Thoughts

Physical sensations

Heart racing
Feeling sick
Needing the toilet
Dry mouth
Sweaty palms

Head ache
Feeling cold
Blinding lights
Tingling
Prickling skin

Tummy ache
Feeling hot
Deafening noises
Jumpy
Sinking tummy

Thoughts

What will happen next?
What is going on?

This is not normal.
I want to go now.

I am safe.
Why am I here?

What are my memories?

This activity will help define the concept of 'memory' for the young person and the idea that physical sensations can be associated with emotional states. It should help the young person begin to understand more clearly their memories and feelings. Subsequent activities will develop the ideas further, but initially they need to be clear about the concept of remembering an event, together with a record of a physical sensation.

Important points to note:
- If the child finds locating memories difficult, try to encourage recollection by asking about key life events (e.g., starting school, moving house).
- It may be helpful to explore carefully some more emotional memories that will have associated physical symptoms.
- It is important that the child feels safe while completing this activity and leaves the exercise feeling positive; it is not designed to trigger any memories of stress the child may have previously experienced.
- Be sure that you feel confident in supporting the child if strong memories arise during the exercise.
- If the child does feel stressed while remembering particular experiences it is important they have support to deal with this after the exercise.
- If the child discloses information during this exercise that concerns you, think about how you will pass this information on and ensure the child receives the correct professional input they need to help them with these experiences.

What are my memories?

Sometimes it is hard to think of things that you have done, or that have happened to you in the past. The things you can think of, or remember, are called memories. A memory can be something that happened a long time ago, for example, a memory could be going to playgroup when you were four years old. A memory can also be thinking of something that happened only yesterday!

When you have important memories, it is helpful to work out what your body was doing and how it felt at the time – this will help identify your feelings. Think of a memory that is important, and think about what your body was doing. Here are some ideas to help you:

- *Memory:* e.g., first day at school; a big disappointment; a holiday; a trip to the zoo; travelling on a boat; my family arguing; a time I got hurt and went to the hospital.

- *What my body was doing, how it felt:* e.g., hot; cold; sweaty; breathing hard; heart pounding; stomach ache; sickness; 'butterflies' in my tummy; weak legs.

Memory	Body
1. _____	_____
2. _____	_____
3. _____	_____
4. _____	_____
5. _____	_____

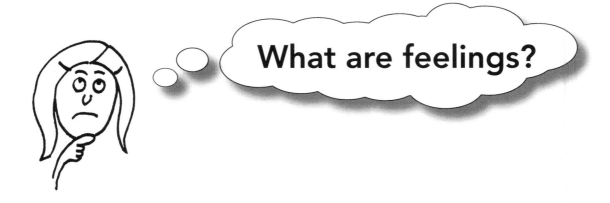

What are feelings?

This activity looks at the words that are used to describe feelings. Some young people find it hard to understand the meaning of words such as 'angry' and 'nervous' and this is an opportunity to find out what they think these words mean.

There may be some need for correction, although it is important to note that there is no definitive right or wrong answer. If the child continues to experience confusion after the exercise it may need to be revisited, or extension activities created which continue to work on these feeling 'labels'.

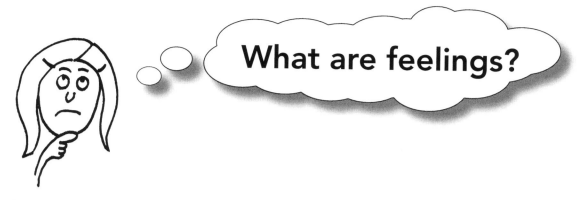

What are feelings?

Sometimes it can be difficult to understand how memories make us feel. Feelings can sometimes difficult to name.

Try to find the words that finish these sentences, so that the feeling matches the activity. Choose from the words in the box at the bottom of the page. Remember, you can use more than one word.

Example:
On Amy's first day at school **she felt** _____. ('worried' OR 'excited')

1. When Andrew was told off by the teacher for not doing his homework **he felt** _____.

2. On her holiday Sarah went skiing for the very first time – she said **she felt really** _____.

3. When Carl was asked to stand up in front of the school and accept his certificate, **he felt** _____.

4. Every day Peter walked to school, following the same route, at the same time, and always saw the same people, and he said **he felt very** _____.

5. When Pamela lost her favourite necklace which her grandmother had given to her **she felt really** _____.

6. Ann stole Mandy's purse from her bag. When Mandy found out **she felt very** _____.

7. Paul was chased home by a big black dog, which barked and tried to bite him several times. When he got home safely **he felt** _____.

Angry	Happy	Relieved	Bored
Sad	Scared	Nervous	Embarrassed
	Worried	Proud	

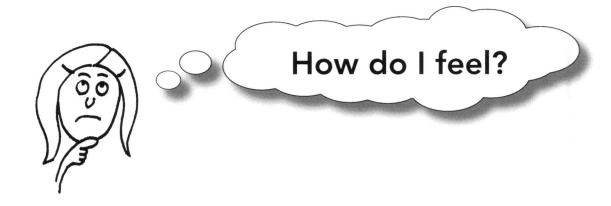

How do I feel?

This exercise allows the youngsters to think about the sorts of feelings and emotions they experience generally, by asking them to circle words that apply to their own feelings.

They may circle some feelings that fit a pattern (i.e., either generally all positive or generally negative) or they may have some feelings that are polar (i.e., extremes of both – angry and excited). This latter response may well indicate a lack of understanding of the meaning of the words, reflecting a lack of emotional knowledge. If a child circles words that are quite disparate in this way it is important to check their understanding of the emotion they are trying to describe.

WHO AM I?

SELF-CONCEPT

MEMORIES

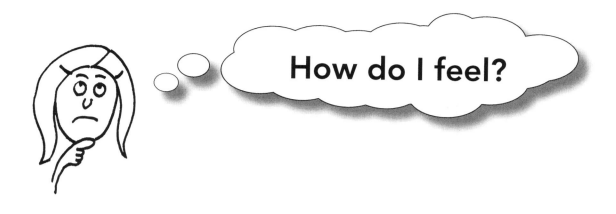

This is an exercise to help find out what sort of feelings you have.

The words listed below describe a wide range of feelings.

Have a look at these words and draw a circle around the ones that you think apply to you and describe how you feel.

happy   sad   **excited**

lonely

DEPRESSED   *worried*
       bored

nervous   PROUD   loud

QUIET   **relieved**

       thoughtful

embarrassed   confused

tired   *relaxed*   *energetic*

       tense

interested   *lost*

       passive   *confident*

aggressive   angry

How do I feel today?

Sometimes you may wish to gauge how the young person feels at the beginning or end of session or on days when they appear more emotional than usual. There is also a need to clarify how the child tends to feel more generally, when they are in a stable mood.

This exercise will explore the child's feelings and emotions at different times of the day, and establish how they view themselves emotionally. This task may reveal unexpected results, for instance where a young person reveals a more vulnerable side. Be cautious with these findings, as they will have a significant bearing on future tasks, in particular low self-esteem can affect the way the young person approaches other activities. Self-esteem will be explored in greater depth in Section 1, Part 2.

Although this is not a standardised self-esteem questionnaire, it will allow you to determine if such a tool is necessary in establishing the mood states of the child. This activity will be an interesting and useful starting point and will help you to determine strengths and weaknesses in the youngster's self-esteem. This in turn will help you to target areas which will support and develop the child's weaknesses, themes which are examined in Section 4 'Developing Skills'.

How do I feel today?

How do you think you are feeling today? Perhaps you are having a good day and are feeling happy! Or maybe you are not so happy – things are going wrong for you.

Take a few minutes to read the following statements and then circle the number from 1 to 5 that fits how you feel:

	Disagree		Agree a Bit		Totally Agree
1. I am usually a very happy person	1	2	3	4	5
2. I tend to cry very easily	1	2	3	4	5
3. I often have bad dreams or nightmares	1	2	3	4	5
4. My friends say I am a happy person	1	2	3	4	5
5. I often have really bad, negative thoughts	1	2	3	4	5
6. I get angry really quickly	1	2	3	4	5
7. Today I feel OK	1	2	3	4	5
8. I find it hard to get a good night's sleep	1	2	3	4	5
9. I am worried for most of the day	1	2	3	4	5
10. I feel loved by my friends and family	1	2	3	4	5
11. I feel very lonely	1	2	3	4	5
12. I tend to smile a lot	1	2	3	4	5

Memories and feelings

This is an exercise to help consolidate the work of previous activities. It will also extend the young person's thinking about developing memories of the feelings associated with different events in their lives.

This is therefore an important task for the child in establishing clear emotions linked to past experiences.

- The child may also learn to re-evaluate previous memories and perceive them more positively, remembering pleasant feelings associated with these experiences.
- This new 'emotional memory bank' will have the benefit of being a useful tool for labelling new memories.
- It can also be used as a benchmark or grading system for new experiences which will help record feelings associated with these.

Memories and feelings

Look at the events you about wrote on **Worksheet 7 'A map of my life'** – you will need to write them in a list on this page – and this time try to remember how you felt with each memory. You can use the list of feelings at the bottom of this page to help if you like. Remember, you may have more than one feeling for each memory.

Memories	Feelings
1. _____	_____
_____	_____
_____	_____
2. _____	_____
_____	_____
_____	_____
3. _____	_____
_____	_____
_____	_____
4. _____	_____
_____	_____
_____	_____
5. _____	_____
_____	_____
_____	_____

Some suggestions of feelings you may have:

Angry	Sad	Happy	Scared
Worried	Relieved	Nervous	Proud
Bored	Embarrassed		

Interests and motivations

The exercises in this section are designed to identify those tasks and activities that the young person enjoys doing. Ideally, these should be activities that the child already engages in, but can also be areas that they may wish to explore further.

Points to consider:
- The youngster may never have considered hobbies and interests;
- Time or available finances may have constrained the opportunity to follow their own pursuits;
- Are there times in the day, week, month or year that are more fruitful for motivation and energy levels – if so why?
- Does the child need other people to accompany or support them for confidence reasons?
- What is stopping the child from pursuing these interests? Are they afraid of failure? Are they easily bored?

The first activity is a general task, asking the young person to agree or disagree with a number of statements relating to interests. This should give a good overview of their level of activity, their interests and how open they are to tackling new or different activities.

Discuss the following with the youngster:
- Do they like to go out and visit new places?
- Are they lacking stimulation in their current lives?
- Are they over-burdened with other activities?
- Have they ever considered what they 'enjoy' doing?

This information can be used to build up a general picture of the child's enthusiasm for activities, as well as giving ideas about what can be used as motivators and rewards for achievement.

Take some time to read the sentences below and think about what you enjoy doing, and why.

Circle the face that most closely represents how you feel about each statement.

1. When I finish my school work I feel very pleased with myself.

2. I always like to reward myself with a special treat for doing well at school.

3. I prefer spending time with my family and friends to playing on my own.

4. I like to play computer games rather than board games with friends.

5. If I could choose my own reward, I would work much harder on school work.

6. If I could choose my own reward, I would work much harder on chores at home.

7. I like to be creative and make my own toys, pictures and activities.

8. I prefer reading a book on my own to going out with family and friends.

My interests and motivations

INTERESTS & MOTIVATIONS

9. I love working with animals.

10. I love teaching others how to do something.

11. I prefer working and playing outdoors.

12. I like to play sports and enjoy physical activity.

13. I like to chat with my friends.

14. I love watching films.

15. I like to go out with my friends and family (to the shops, the cinema or for meals).

16. I like to prepare food for my family.

17. I like to have a day out somewhere, with a picnic and a walk.

18. I like to visit museums, castles and historic sites.

My energy levels

This is a simple exercise to establish when the young person has the most energy and enthusiasm for tasks.

It can be important to know these daily, weekly and monthly rhythms so that in the future targets can be set for completion at times most likely to achieve success.

My energy levels

There are some times during the day, week or year when you feel most energetic and able to do more. Some people find they are most awake first thing in the morning and able to concentrate and work really well at this time. Others prefer the afternoon or the evening.

Take a few minutes to think about the best times of the day, week and year for you. Are you a morning person? Are you a summer or winter person?

Try to fill in the boxes below to work out your best times to work and get things done!

During the day	Time	For how long
Completing written tasks		
Doing physical activity		
Listening and concentrating		
Chatting to friends and family		
Watching TV, computers etc		
During the week/month	**Day**	**Month / time of year**
Completing written tasks		
Doing physical activity		
Listening and concentrating		
Chatting to friends and family		
Watching TV, computers etc		

This should give you an idea of when you can really set yourself challenges to help reach your goals!

Make a note of your key times – these are when you will really be able to do your best!

My hobbies

This is an opportunity for the young person to reflect on what they are currently interested in, as well as identifying any gaps, and those hobbies they would like to explore further.

Examples of hobby topics are provided which can be explored with the child. Think as creatively as possible here, exploring wide ranging ideas and trying not to typecast the youngster. It may be that they could excel at a variety of interests and activities which they have never previously considered. Give them an opportunity to 'think big' and perhaps challenge them with sports, activities and interests they have only previously experienced through television.

This exercise does not necessarily lead to any commitment to these activities at this stage, the idea is to identify interests for consideration later on.

My hobbies

You may have interests and activities that you like to spend time on. You might read or learn about a topic you find interesting, or spend time playing a sport or building a collection. For instance, learning about dinosaurs, stamp collecting, bird watching or canoeing.

Take a few minutes to think about the hobbies you have, and then any others you would be interested in finding out more about, and write them in the boxes below.

My Hobbies

Things I would be interested in

Hobby topics			
Sports	Engineering	Creativity	Outdoors
Events	Collecting	Nature	Therapeutic
Science	History	Languages	Foreign countries

Who are my friends?

When working with children and young people it is important to establish the extent of their support networks. Children who undertake activities in isolation are less likely to succeed and make progress. If the young person has other people to talk to, share and support them through their personal development, they will grow more confidently.

This activity could touch upon sensitive issues for the youngster as they may have few friends and may not trust those they have.

- Try to establish the extent of the child's social network and if possible some of the issues which may exist for them around friendships.
- The end of the exercise is designed to offer positive outcomes to their peer relationships (e.g., how they can help others).
- You should ensure that the child leaves the session feeling confident and self-assured.

Who are my friends?

Most people have friends to talk to and who can help out when they have problems. Some friends will go to school with you, others might live near you or even far away and you will see them at different times. Friends are important in helping you to enjoy life and feel part of group.

Do you have friends? Who are they? When did you meet? What do you do with your friends? Do you share similar interests, sense of humour or experiences together?

Try to complete the following activity and identify your best friends.

My friends at school are: _____

My friends who live near me at home are: _____

My friends at clubs and groups I attend are: _____

Other friends *(those who live further away or friends of the family)*: _____

MY FRIENDS

My closest friends   *What we have in common*

- _____   _____

- _____   _____

- _____   _____

- _____   _____

Friends that could help me if I need them: _____

Things they do to help me: _____

What else they could do to help me: _____

Who else I would like to be my friend: _____

What they could do to help me: _____

What I could do to help them: _____

What do my friends think of me?

Building on the last exercise, this is an opportunity for the young person to unpack some of their thoughts around how their friends view them. It will begin to establish the child's view of themselves as seen by others. This may differ wildly from reality and will link in with some of the self-esteem issues raised in previous activities.

It may be necessary to complete this activity more than once if the youngster provides very confused or inaccurate information. Either use a clean copy of the worksheet, or a different coloured pen on the second occasion and ensure that you question and challenge the child's perceptions:

- What makes you think they see you as …?
- Who thinks you are …?
- Why would 'x' consider you to be …?
- Look at some of the other words here – do you think anyone would think you could be … / … / …?

What do my friends think of me?

This is an exercise to help you think about how your friends view you.

Look at the words below and draw a circle around the ones that you think describe how your best or closest friends see you.

When you have done this, change the colour of your pen, and now circle the words you think describe how other friends, who don't know you as well, see you.

aggressive

happy

MOODY

selfish

energetic

nasty

helpful

LOUD

unkind

unhappy

QUIET

fun

naughty

giggly

bubbly

kind

shy

honest

What am I good at?

This activity is another exercise in self-exploration and will deepen your knowledge around how the young person views their skills and talents.

As the young person will probably divide their life between home and school, it is good to establish their perceptions of skills in both settings. You may find that this exercise needs to allow for additional skills to be identified and rated, so the activity can be extended to explore this further by using a larger sheet of paper and more rating scales.

The task uses a 'solution-focused' approach which asks the young person to rate their performances in the present and also where they wish to be in the future. It then identifies the road blocks the child may perceive as stopping them from achieving their goals, as well as identifying the strategies which help them to gain success.

This activity can be very beneficial as it not only establishes the child's perceptions of their skills, but identifies how they came to acquire them and the way these strategies can be used fruitfully in achieving new goals.

What am I good at?

This is an exercise to find out what you feel you are good at – your skills and talents! Take a few minutes to think of some of the things you can do well and also something you find difficult.

Something I do well at school is: _____

Rate yourself on a scale for how good you are:
(0 = not good / 5 = very good)

0	1	2	3	4	5

Something I do well outside of school is: _____

Rate yourself on a scale for how good you are:
(0 = not good / 5 = very good)

0	1	2	3	4	5

Something I would like to be better at is: _____

Use a circle to rate how good you are now, and then use a cross to show where you would like to be in a few months time:

0	1	2	3	4	5

What is it that stops me making progress with this?

_____

What helped you to be good at the things you listed in questions 1 and 2? Write your ideas below:

_____
_____

How can I get better and reach my 'target' for the activity in question 3?

_____

Who can help me to reach my target?

_____

Who am I?

Understanding a young person's level of self-esteem is crucial. A young person's poor view of themselves can undermine most areas of work as it can reduce motivation and expectations of success.

A good level of self-esteem increases the young person's chances of success socially and will enable them to tackle new problems with confidence and motivation.

What do I value in myself?

This is a very broad introduction which gently tests, in broad terms, the young person's view of themselves.

It begins to look at the young person's physical, emotional, intellectual and performance perspectives of themselves and offers them a positive starting point for looking at who they are. This is important as touching on such sensitive and personal information should not be completed cold; the child needs to feel safe.

What do I value in myself?

Sometimes you might not feel very good about yourself, even though you are really good at lots of things.

It is important to make sure you do feel good and celebrate your strengths! You are worth it!

Take a few minutes to work out what you really like about yourself:

What I like about me:

- _____
- _____
- _____
- _____
- _____
- _____
- _____
- _____

(Examples: sense of humour; my face / body / legs etc.; sporting skills; artistic skills; my smile; my personality; my school achievements; my quietness)

If I had to pick one thing that I really like about myself it would be:

- _____

I have chosen this because _____

How do I feel today?

Sometimes you may wish to gauge how the young person feels at the beginning or end of session or on days when they appear more emotional than usual. There is also a need to clarify how the child tends to feel more generally, when they are in a stable mood.

This exercise will explore the child's feelings and emotions at different times of the day, and establish how they view themselves emotionally. This task may reveal unexpected results, for instance where a young person reveals a more vulnerable side. Be cautious with these findings, as they will have a significant bearing on future tasks, in particular low self-esteem can affect the way the young person approaches other activities.

Although this is not a standardised self-esteem questionnaire, it will allow you to determine if such a tool is necessary in establishing the mood states of the child. This activity will be an interesting and useful starting point and will help you to determine strengths and weaknesses in the youngster's self-esteem. This in turn will help you to target areas which will support and develop the child's weaknesses, themes which are examined in Section 4 'Developing Skills'.

N.B. This is a repetition of Worksheet 12, which you may not have completed previously. It is important to find out how the young person feels at different times as they may experience mood changes which can then be compared across sessions.

How do I feel today?

How do you think you are feeling today? Perhaps you are having a good day and are feeling happy! Or maybe you are not so happy – things are going wrong for you.

Take a few minutes to read the following statements and then circle the number from 1 to 5 that fits how you feel:

	Disagree		Agree a Bit		Totally Agree
1. I am usually a very happy person	1	2	3	4	5
2. I tend to cry very easily	1	2	3	4	5
3. I often have bad dreams or nightmares	1	2	3	4	5
4. My friends say I am a happy person	1	2	3	4	5
5. I often have really bad, negative thoughts	1	2	3	4	5
6. I get angry really quickly	1	2	3	4	5
7. Today I feel OK	1	2	3	4	5
8. I find it hard to get a good night's sleep	1	2	3	4	5
9. I am worried for most of the day	1	2	3	4	5
10. I feel loved by my friends and family	1	2	3	4	5
11. I feel very lonely	1	2	3	4	5
12. I tend to smile a lot	1	2	3	4	5

This is an easy exercise that requires the young person to rate statements on a scale of 'agree' to 'disagree'.

Try to encourage them to be honest in completing this task and not to 'put on a brave face' or answer with neutral responses that neither agree or disagree. Encourage the child to complete the scale a second time if you feel that they are withholding their true perception of themselves.

Points to note:

- The information obtained here should be very informative in helping to uncover more of how the child thinks others may view them.
- This is a broad tool that examines aspects of school life as well as general perspectives.
- This scale does not investigate views of family members as these have previously been addressed.
- If, however, there are key family members who have a heavy bearing on how the child views themselves this will become clear during this task.

Sometimes it's good to know that others value things about you too! It could be that different people in your life like different things about you.

Read the statements below, thinking about what other people would say about you and decide whether you agree or disagree with each one. Now circle the face that is closest to your answer.

People like my sense of humour.

I have lots of friends who like being with me.

I am good fun to be with.

I am good at listening.

I help people out when they are sad or have problems.

My friends think I am reliable and they can depend on me.

People say I am chatty and talk a lot.

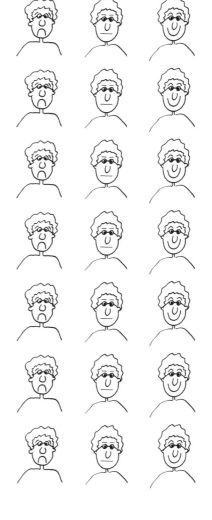

What do others like about me?

People like the way I look.

I have friends who like to spend time with me.

People who know me say I have lots of good skills and qualities.

People say I am caring and helpful.

I am good at thinking up games and activities for my friends to play.

My friends prefer to spend time with me in small groups, or on my own.

I am popular at school.

People think I am good at school work.

I have more friends outside of school than in school.

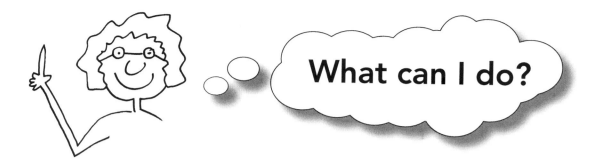

What can I do?

This activity moves on to more practical tasks by asking the young person to recall specifics about what they are good at. It is positively framed so that even a child with very poor self-esteem will have to think about their successes.

Points to note:

- Encourage the young person to be positive in their responses, mentioning even their smallest successes.
- The achievements identified by the child do not need to be very recent.
- It may be that in the past the young person has had a variety of skills and achievements and these should be used as a window into their 'old' self.
- The idea of this exercise is to leave the young person feeling empowered by their interests and skills, no matter how minor they may seem.
- Try to ensure that the child ends this exercise feeling better about themselves than when they started it.

What can I do?

Sometimes you might forget the things you can do well - how talented you are! Read the sentences below and try to think of examples of things you can do. Write them on the worksheet.

Remind yourself of how skilled you are!

Think of a sport, activity or game that you enjoy and play well (running, swimming, card games, snakes and ladders, football).

_____

_____

Name something you made in art and crafts that you liked (painting, clothes making, cooking, model making).

_____

_____

Think of a person you have helped recently. Who was it and what did you do?

_____

_____

Which chores and activities do you help with at home?

_____

_____

Think of a time when you were chatting to someone and made them laugh. What did you say?

_____

_____

Think of a time when you got a reward and praise, what did you do to earn it?

_____

_____

Think of a lesson or a time in school when you did well – what did you do?

_____

_____

What makes me feel good?

The idea of this exercise is to try to identify the positive times in the young person's life when they have felt safe, happy and relaxed.

To help the youngster think along the right lines a selection of statements are presented as prompts, but they will probably have their own ideas and may also need to dig around in their memories.

Try to encourage the young person to think about:

- Different times in the day, week and year; perhaps there are occasions that form regular patterns.
- People they may spend time with only occasionally.
- Places they like to visit.
- Activities they enjoy.

They may have unrealistic ideas about what it is to feel 'happy' – this is a concept that can be confusing and may feel unobtainable. Try to get the child to grasp the positive moments in their life with pleasure.

What makes me feel good?

There are times in your life when you feel really good! Happy, relaxed and safe.

It is important to know what makes you feel like this so that you can plan 'good' times for the future. This may be when you need a reward, a break or just feel like doing something you enjoy!

Take a few minutes to work out the times when you feel good, and which activities and people help you to feel good.

Here are some ideas to get you thinking!

Circle the statements that apply to you or write down your own ideas.

A holiday   A party   A school trip

Spending time with my friends   Spending time with my family

A visit to the zoo or wildlife park   Going to the cinema

Watching TV at home   Eating my favourite food

Playing sport   Doing my school work

Playing on my bike   Playing a musical instrument

Listening to music   Drawing and painting

Playing computer games   Going for a walk

Playing with my pets   Helping others

Achieving a goal   Learning a new skill   Reading

Section 2

About Other People

About other people

This section examines how the young person regards other children and adults. It will review their perception of other people's communication styles. If the young person has a genuine communication difficulty it will quickly become apparent through the following exercises.

Many of the tasks involve the use of pictures and require the child to study social scenarios, thinking about how people talk to each other. It begins by considering the structure of conversations and then reviewing the different aspects of communication in turn.

About other people

Now that you have a good idea of who you are, you need to begin to look at the other people around you.

- What is it that makes you like spending time with certain people?
- Do some people do things that you don't like?
- How do other people behave?
- Are there things you could learn about how other people make friends?

These are some of the questions you will work on in this section 'About Other People'.

You will do some of this:

 Looking at pictures of groups of people.

Looking at and drawing cartoons and pictures of people.

Looking at pictures of everyday scenes and events.

Then you will also have a chance to think about some of these things:

 Why do you trust some people and not others?

How do people talk to each other?

What makes a good conversation?

 What is 'chatting'?

 What happens when talking goes wrong?

 What is trust?

These exercises and activities will help you to look more carefully at the conversations around you and see some of the important things that go into helping people 'chat' successfully!

Let's get started!

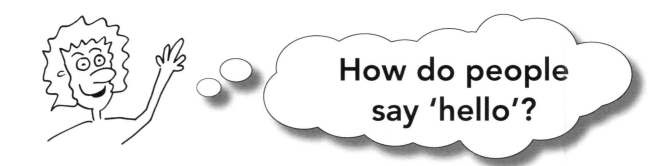

How do people say 'hello'?

This is a simple activity that encourages the young person to think about their initial greetings when talking to other people. It aims to start them thinking about general introductions and the mechanics of starting communication with others.

Points to note:

- Try to get the child to be open and honest.
- Encourage them to be descriptive and give full answers.
- Do they need to think about their recent experiences to answer questions?
- Are there any cultural or social issues that the child is unaware of?
- What are these?

How do people say 'hello'?

This is an activity to get you thinking about different ways to say 'hello' and how you might greet different people in different ways.

How do you say 'hello' on the telephone? How do you say 'hello' to your best friends? Would you say 'hello' to someone you have never met before in the same way? Have a go at answering the following questions!

Remember – saying 'hello' is a greeting!

1. How do you say 'hello' to your mum, dad or a close member of your family?

   _____

2. How do you answer the telephone?

   _____

3. What do you say when you meet someone for the first time?

   _____

4. How do you greet your best friend?

   _____

5. How do you greet someone very important to you who you haven't seen for ages?

   _____

6. How does a shop assistant or waitress say 'hello' to you – what do they say?

   _____

7. How would you greet The Queen?

   _____

8. How would you say 'hello' to someone you don't like very much?

   _____

9. What do people do when they say 'hello' to each other in France or Italy?

   _____

How do people say 'goodbye'?

This activity will help the young person review the way they leave people and end conversations.

It will echo the previous task around introductions, by focusing on similar scenarios and building on their knowledge of those situations.

Points to note:

- Ensure the child is honest/open in their answers.
- Encourage the youngster to give clear and full answers.
- Encourage reflection on recent experiences.
- What cultural and social issues is the child presenting?

How do people say 'goodbye'?

It is important to know how people leave one another and the different ways to say 'goodbye'. Take a few minutes to answer some of these questions to get a clearer idea about how you think people say 'goodbye'.

1. How do you say 'goodbye' to someone you really care about who you are not going to see for a long time?

   _____

2. How do people say goodbye on the phone?

   _____

3. How do shop assistants or waitresses say goodbye to people?

   _____

4. What do people do when they leave each other in France or Italy?

   _____

5. How do you say goodbye to your close friends?

   _____

6. How do you leave someone you don't like very much?

   _____

7. How would you leave The Queen?

   _____

8. How would you ask someone to leave that you don't like?

   _____

9. How do you say goodbye to someone you've only just met?

   _____

How do you talk with your body?

This task will help to identify whether the young person can correctly interpret meanings conveyed through body language, by matching statements and cartoon images.

If the responses given are good then the child is clearly able to identify the meanings expressed through body language, but may have some issues with giving the correct responses. If, however, they are not able to link the statements to the correct pictures then they will need additional tutoring on reading body language.

Points to note:

- Is the child scanning posture, facial expression and the positions of arms and legs?
- What are they using to interpret the message?
- Are they able to use body language themselves to copy the stance or expression? If so, how does it make them feel?

How do you talk with your body?

The way that you stand, walk, sit and hold your position tells other people a lot about how you feel and what you are thinking.

This is important because other people will decide what to say to you, and how to say it, by 'reading' what you feel or think from your body language.

You also need to be good at reading other people's body language as this will help you have better conversations with people, make friends, and get on with others.

This activity will help you to work out how your body 'talks'. Look at the pictures on the next page and try to work out which statement goes with which picture.

	Picture
John was really angry about the outcome.	_____
Peter is bored and wants to leave.	_____
Nobody knew anyone …	_____
Fred was really pleased to have come first.	_____
The joke was really funny and everyone thought so.	_____
Jane feels really nervous and worried.	_____

BODY LANGUAGE

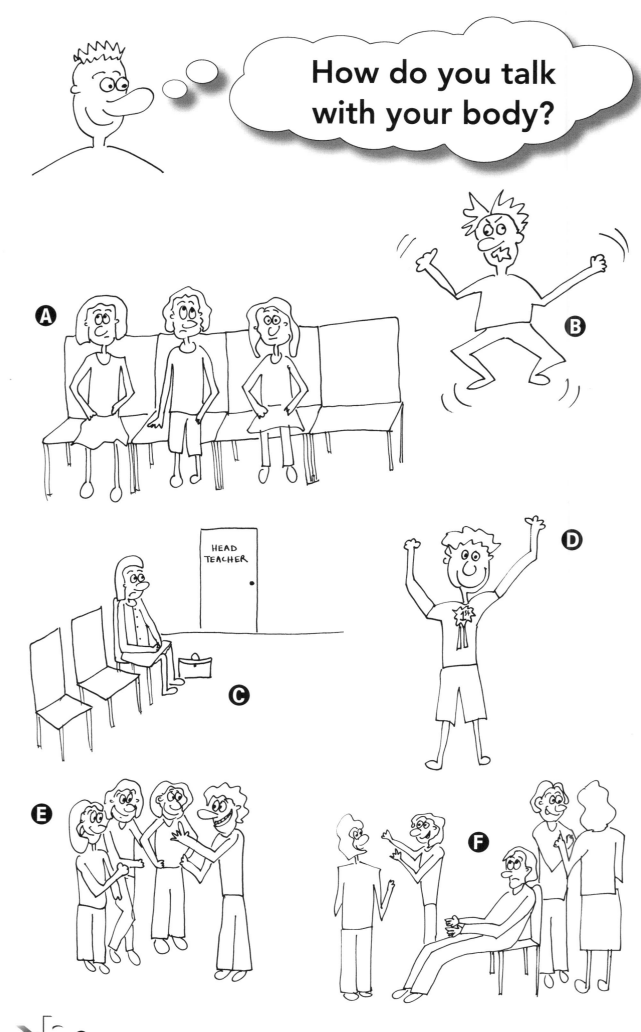

Practicing body language

This activity will build on the information gained in the previous exercise. Use the pictures provided to explore different scenarios with the youngster, asking them to apply their understanding to decode the different situations.

This activity can be extended through the use of additional pictures or photographs that you could collect together with the child.

Points to note:

- Try to make this fun.
- There is no right or wrong answer. The answer given can be a prompt for further discussion.
- Try to encourage the child to scan and use all the information (perhaps even the obvious signs that we take for granted).
- Ask the child to give full descriptions of both thoughts and feelings.

Practicing body language

This is an exercise to help you practice your body language skills.

Look at the pictures below and try to work out what you think each picture is trying to tell you about what the people are thinking and how they feel. There is no right or wrong answer – make your best guess!

Think: _____

Feel: _____

Think: _____

Feel: _____

Think: _____

Feel: _____

Think: _____

Feel: _____

Think: _____

Feel: _____

Think: _____

Feel: _____

How do you talk with your face?

This exercise will examine more closely how well the young person is able to interpret facial expressions. Some children may be good at identifying simple emotions such as sad or happy. However, many will have difficulty in identifying more complex expressions, such as confusion, worry, relief or tiredness.

The task becomes increasingly complex with more challenging and ambiguous facial expressions to decode.

Points to note:

- Encourage the child to have a go at decoding the faces, even if they don't know what they mean
- Ask the child how they are making decisions about their interpretations.
- Are they scanning all of the elements of the face?
- Are they able to copy the facial expression in the picture? If so how does it make them feel?

How do you talk with your face?

Your face can tell other people a lot about how you feel and what you are thinking.

The expressions on someone's face are very important. When people are trying to understand what is being said they tend to use the look on your face more than the actual words you say.

For this reason you need to be sure that the look on your face matches your words when you talk to someone. You should also make sure that you don't just listen to what people say, but look at their faces when they say it.

In this activity you have to match the statements to the faces – so that the spoken words match the looks on the faces.

Expression

1. "I am really embarrassed." _____
2. "I am so sad." _____
3. "Hmm. Let me think." _____
4. "Oh dear, that's not good." _____
5. "Hey, what do you think you are doing!" _____
6. "That's nice." _____
7. "Brilliant! Great news!" _____
8. "I've had an idea!" _____
9. "I don't like that." _____
10. "That tastes bad!" _____
11. "Oh! That made me jump!" _____
12. "I like you. Let's be friends." _____

How do you talk with your face?

A

B

C

D

E

F

G

H

I

J

K

L

Chatting and hanging out

This is an introductory task to get the child thinking about social conversations.

It may be quite a daunting task for some youngsters who find conversation very difficult – be aware of those who do not understand the difference between a social conversation (chatting) and factual information gathering. For instance, some youngsters may be quite skilled at finding out facts and figures relating to events or objects (e.g., train timetables or engine capacity). However, they may find it difficult to ask appropriately about a person's health, mood or current situation – chatting.

Chatting will be examined in greater detail in the section 'About Me with Others'.

Chatting and hanging out

These worksheets will help you work on how people talk in social situations: in other words 'chatting'. These are general conversations that you have with people which are not planned, and which are seen as enjoyable and fun by those who are chatting.

Try to think of a time recently when you may have had a 'chatty' conversation. Who were you talking to and where? What did you talk about? Write some of your thoughts about the conversation below:

It is important that you are able to enjoy and join in chatty conversations, as they will help you to build relationships and make friends.

What does chatting look like?

This activity will help the youngster to organise their understanding of social talking into social contexts. The idea of the exercise is to expose them to various social scenarios through comic strips which make the situations simple, visual and fun. The child can then fill in the blanks with appropriate social responses.

It may help to:

- Give the youngster free rein for the first few exercises to see what sort of responses they come up with.
- Offer some guidance and encouragement as the exercise progresses.
- Explain there are no right or wrong answers, so they cannot fail.
- Use this as an opportunity to find out how the child interprets situations socially rather than trying to 'teach' them skills.
- Record any unusual responses and challenge inappropriate comments at the end of the activity.

This is an exercise to help you work out what people do when they are chatting to each other.

Look at the cartoon strips below and try to think of some chatty comments to add to the last cartoon picture.

'Hello Jamie.'

'Hello Steve.'

'How are you?'

'I'm fine, thank you.'

'Did you watch TV last night?'

'_____.'

'Hello, Andrew.'

'Hello. I haven't seen you for some time.'

'I've been on holiday. We went to Spain.'

'Was the weather nice?'

'_____
_____?'

'_____
_____.'

What does chatting look like?

'Hello, Catherine speaking.'

'I'm at home. And you?'

'_____

_____?'

'Hi, it's John. Where are you?'

'Same. Do you want to come for a coffee?'

'_____

_____.'

'Hi Charlie.'

'Yes. Have you got new trainers?'

'_____

_____?'

'Hi. Is that new kit?'

'Yes, Mum got them for me this week.'

'_____

_____.'

Reading a social picture

This is an extension of the 'chatting' exercises in which suggested solutions are given to the child, so they can match them to the scenarios. As this is picture-based exercise and uses simple cartoons it will appeal to youngsters and maintain their levels of interest.

Points to note:

- Try to work out how the child is making decisions about which answer corresponds to which cartoon.
- Offer encouragement, challenges and questions as needed.
- Offer the youngster helpful strategies where necessary, such as encouraging them to scan the scene, look at facial expressions and body language.
- Ask the child to list the 'clues' they are using and to keep note of these.
- Offer the correct answer when the young person is stuck or unable to label correctly. However, ensure this is done in a sensitive manner and framed so that the child feels they achieved a degree of success.

Reading a social picture

It is very useful to be able to look at groups of people and make sense of the situation without having to talk to anyone. The idea is to try to understand what is happening just by looking at what is going on.

To help you get better at this these activities use pictures of different situations. Look at each picture and then choose from the list a phrase that you think matches the picture.

See if you can match these pictures to the right phrase in the box below:

	Picture
1. "I am so bored – I wish I could leave."	_____
2. "I want a go now – why do I have to wait?"	_____
3. "I think they are lying, they won't look at me when they speak."	_____
4. "I'm really worried, I might have missed it."	_____
5. "What happens next? I can't understand what's being said."	_____

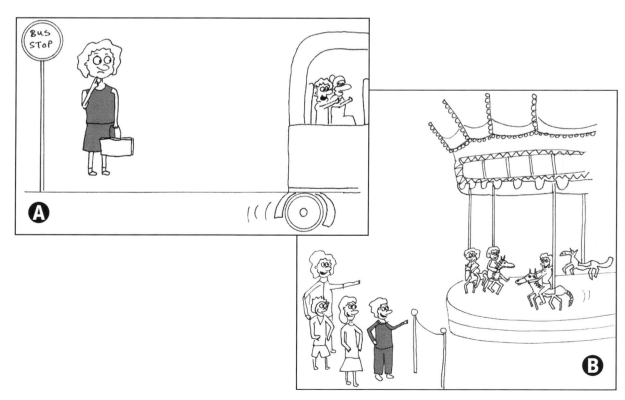

Reading a social picture

Finding your way

This is an opportunity to further establish the young person's scanning skills and ensure they are 'reading' images accurately. It also examines their ability to concentrate and follow an instruction and therefore will help uncover any language issues around comprehension. This exercise should reveal any possible comprehension difficulties which may need further assessment.

Points to note:

- Try reading the instructions aloud and see if the child can follow them when presented orally.
- If the youngster has problems remembering instructions try breaking them down into 'chunks' to see if that helps.
- Is the child able to locate places on the map? If not, what is hindering their performance?

Extension Task
- Is this an exercise the child might need to complete in real life, with adult support? Would it help to visit somewhere to try to follow instructions for real to develop these skills? Does the youngster feel overwhelmed by the thought of this? How do they negotiate their way around the school / new buildings / trips to new places?

Finding your way

This is an activity designed to help you find your way around a map using directions. See if you can work out where the following directions will lead you:

1. Leave the supermarket and turn left. At the crossroads turn right.

   • Where are you? _____

2. Start at the pond. Turn right at the 'T' junction. Follow the road to the traffic light. Turn right, take the first turning on the right.

   • Where are you? _____

3. Leave the bus station, turning right. Follow the road to the 'T' junction and turn right. Follow the road and take the third shop entrance on the right-hand side.

   • Where are you? _____

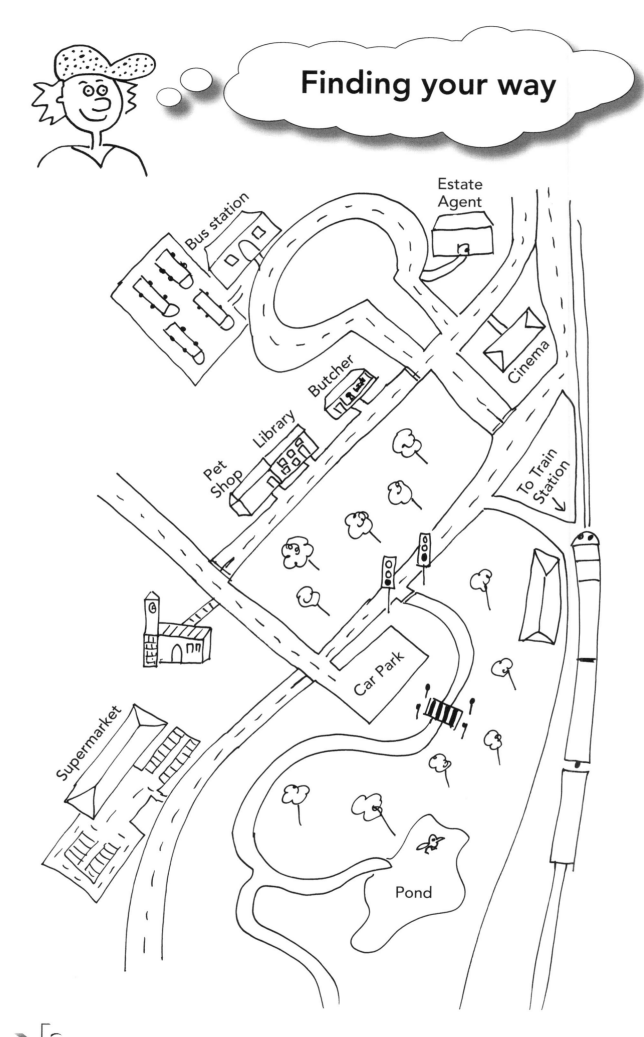

Finding your way

Remember what you see

This activity builds on the previous one, by using an image of a busy street and tasks involving scanning, interpretation and memory. Through the use of questions, this activity will help you check that the child is able to perceive all the visual information in their environment and use it to interpret situations.

Some of the questions require factual recall of names, times and positions of objects. Others may require more interpretation and being able to put yourself in another's situation, linking to empathy and 'Theory of Mind' (Wing,1996).

Points to note:

- The youngster may demonstrate strengths of visual memory here – how could these be used to their advantage in social situations? Can the child build up mental representations of places they have visited? Are these accurate and can they be used to describe situations to others?
- Does the youngster have difficulty with this task or certain of its elements? What are they able to remember when you give them a second opportunity to complete the task? Are they more successful?
- What sorts of information does the child recall accurately and where are they making mistakes? Is there a pattern?
- What can you deduce about the child from this activity? How do you think the youngster would learn to remember information based on this activity?

Remember what you see

The following activity is about trying to remember what you see – do you take notice of the things around you?

Take two minutes to look carefully at the picture on the next page – really study it! Then turn over the page and try to answer as many questions about the picture as you can from memory. When you have finished look at the picture again and see how many of your answers were right.

1. What time is showing on the clock tower?

2. Could the children on the pedestrian crossing see the mailbox?

3. How many children are carrying a balloon?

4. How many birds are flying in the sky?

5. What are the removal men carrying?

6. Can the crossing patrol warden see the newsagent?

7. How many metres is it to the toilets?

8. Can the children with balloons see the cinema?

9. How many miles is it to Winton?

10. Is the pedestrian crossing warden a man or a woman?

11. Who is leaving the restaurant?

12. What is showing at the cinema?

13. Can the boy with the dog see the removal men?

14. Can the crossing patrol warden see the clock tower?

Remember what you see

What are they trying to say?

In this activity the youngster is required to guess at possible verbal exchanges and write them under the cartoons. This will require them to read each character's facial expression and body language. As there is no right or wrong answer the child need not fear failure. It is also a good activity to complete together with the youngster if they are finding the task a challenge.

Points to note:

- Ask the child to suggest feelings that could be expressed (e.g., cross, angry, furious, content, happy, funny) and write them in with pencil.
- Now ask the child to make up a sentence about the emotion they have identified. This can be very simple, such as 'You make me feel very angry.' and a response of 'I'm so sorry.'
- The hard work will be identifying and labelling the emotion.
- Find out what, if anything, the child finds difficult in this process – is it labelling the emotion or putting together a sentence?
- Use this task to assess what the youngster struggles with and how they can best overcome these difficulties, as well as how you can help them.

What are they trying to say?

Looking at pictures can tell us a lot about what is happening between people – we can use the things we see to tell us how people feel and what might be going on between them.

In this activity you will look at pictures and try to guess how the people feel and what they are saying to each other. Write your ideas underneath.

'Oh no!'
'Don't worry, I'll buy
another one.'

This exercise is designed to discover how the youngster interprets not just a situation or a facial expression, but the possible links between the two. Here they must connect a social trigger with a corresponding feeling and emotion.

The child may have been able to label a feeling, read a facial expression and scan a picture, but can they relate these to the social situation and predict why someone would feel a certain way?

Points to note:

- Does the youngster scan the picture and pick up on the relevant information?
- Do they 'miss out' certain pieces of information?
- Are they able to label the information correctly?
- What helps the child correct mistakes?

Predicting how someone feels

This is an exercise designed to help you think about how people might feel about a situation they find themselves in.

Perhaps you find it quite difficult to imagine how someone else would feel – these activities will to help you try to get better at seeing things from someone else's perspective.

Look at the pictures and work out how you think the people in them are feeling. There are no right or wrong answers! Write down your ideas underneath each picture.

'I'm so cross!'
_____

_____
_____

_____
_____

_____
_____

_____
_____

_____
_____

This activity involves a series of cartoons and requires the youngster to rearrange images in order for the stories to make sense. The young person must read the pictures carefully and use their knowledge of the world and life events to sequence them correctly.

The cartoons are of increasing complexity, and require the youngster not only to scan thoroughly and process the information sequentially, but to spot differences and relate the story to real life.

Points to note:

- Can the youngster scan thoroughly and detect details?
- What errors are they making?
- Do they spend a long time on this task?
- What are they using to determine their responses and solutions?
- How can you best support the youngster in this task?

Put me in the right order!

This activity will help you to read pictures of events and put them in the right order. The pictures in the cartoons below are all muddled up, and need to be put in the right order.

See if you can work out the right order for the following cartoons, writing the numbers 1,2 and 3 in the correct sequence in the boxes.

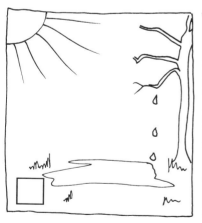

1 of 2

PREDICTING WHAT WILL HAPPEN NEXT

Put me in the right order!

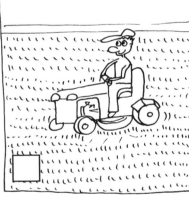

Predicting what will happen next

If the youngster is able to scan and interpret social scenes then they will also need to be able to predict outcomes based on their own experiences. This task will establish how well a youngster is able to link cause and effect using a selection of visually appealing pictures and scenes of everyday activities.

Points to note:

- Can the young person 'read' the scenario?
- Are they able to determine what will happen next?
- What sorts of errors are they making?
- Do they show awareness of the social situations? Have they witnessed any of these scenarios or experienced any similar ones themselves?
- If so – how did they feel afterwards? This is an extension that may help you to link discussion about emotions with social situations.

Predicting what will happen next

This activity that will ask you to plan what is likely to happen next. In the cartoons below, the last picture is missing. Look at the pictures and draw or write in the last box what you think is going to happen next!

Have a go!

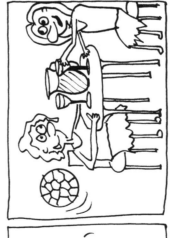

Predicting what will happen next

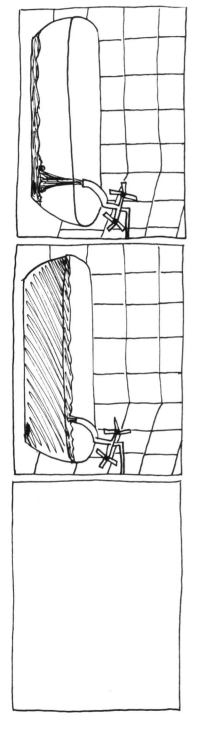

Have a go at drawing a cartoon strip in the last row of empty boxes.
You can use stick people in your cartoon if this helps.

Making a mistake

Quite often young people can interpret a situation incorrectly because they have assumed that there was malicious intent behind the action.

This activity encourages the youngster to understand that we are all subject to error and can make mistakes. It will also help the child to relate an incident as a 'mistake' and support them in understanding that mistakes are OK.

Points to note:

- Encourage the child to talk about an incident and how it could have been a mistake.
- Explain that we all make mistakes and that this is OK.
- Try to establish how the youngster responds to mistakes they have made – do they apologise?
- Examine how they respond when others make mistakes – does the child 'forgive' people who make mistakes? Can they understand that mistakes happen?

Making a mistake

Sometimes people make mistakes and can say or do something which is wrong and upsets you.

There may be times when you say or do the wrong thing, and this gets you into trouble. Have you ever done something that has upset someone? Perhaps you have said something that annoyed somebody?

This activity is about those times when someone has upset you, or maybe you have made a mistake.

See if you can finish the following sentences about making mistakes.

1. Somebody at school upset me once because they _____
    _____

2. The last time someone said 'sorry' to me was _____
    _____

3. I get annoyed with people in conversations when they don't
    _____
    _____

4. The last time I upset someone I _____
    _____

5. My family say I annoy them when I _____
    _____

6. The last time I said sorry was because _____
    _____

7. I often make mistakes in conversations with people when I _____
    _____

8. The people who annoy me most are usually _____
    _____

The concept of trust is an important one for young people to establish, as they need to believe in significant others with whom they have safe and positive relationships.

It is important to identify the people who the child trusts and who are trustworthy.

- What makes the relationship / person trustworthy? Should the child trust this person?
- Is the child able to be trusted themselves? What makes you feel this?
- Is trust an issue for this child? Have they been badly treated by others? Are they confused about the concept of trust?
- What mistakes is the child making about trust? How can you support the child in developing trusting relationships?

Trust is a difficult word to understand. It is very important that people know what it means so that everyone feels safer in their friendships with other people.

What do you think trust means? When someone says they trust you, what are they saying? Who do you trust?

Take a few minutes to write your thoughts below:

_____

_____

_____

_____

_____

_____

_____

_____

_____

Most people would agree that trust is a bond between people in friendships, and means that they feel safe with that person. They do not do things on purpose that would upset, hurt or make the other person feel angry.

Read the following statements and try to answer whether they are true or false. If you are not sure how you feel, you can answer 'Don't know'. Remember, there are no right or wrong answers!

True/False/Don't know

1. You can usually trust your family to help you out in a crisis. _____

2. You must trust your friends. _____

3. Trust can only be earned. _____

4. People can always trust me. _____

5. I only trust someone if I have known them for at least a year. _____

6. Someone who breaks your trust and upsets you can never be trusted again. _____

7. If you don't trust someone you don't like them. _____

8. Most people cannot be trusted. _____

9. I trust my parents more than anyone else. _____

10. If someone lies to you they cannot be trusted. _____

11. My teachers trust me. _____

Section 3

About Me with Others

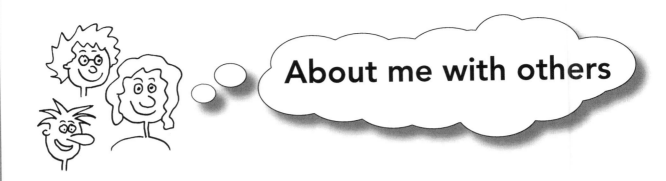

About me with others

This section will enable you to establish a young person's specific areas of weakness in their communication with others. It will examine many aspects of their communication style, looking at who the young person has conversations with, where and with whom they can talk more successfully and what they find most challenging.

When working through these activities a 'communication map' will become clear; this will allow you to focus on areas that go well and those requiring more input.

About me with others

In these activities you will be taking a good look at how you talk, play and work with other people.

This section will ask questions such as:

- What do I do well with other people?

- What do I enjoy with others?

- Am I outgoing, sociable and chatty?

- What do I need to get better at?

There may be some things that you are brilliant at doing with other people, perhaps in school, or at home with your family. It is important to identify these things, so that you can build on your successes!

It is also good to try to set goals and find areas where you can do better, and think about who can help you with this.

How do you say 'hello' to people?

This is a good reflective activity that introduces young people to the idea that they have casual conversations with people on an everyday basis. It will help to identify the people that the youngster talks to, how, when and with what outcome.

Points to note:

- Try to find examples that differ in location and content of discussion.
- This variety of social exchange will help the young person to see how differently they may be viewed when having informal discussions.
- Does the young person find it difficult to think of examples? If so, why is this? (Does this correspond with limited social contact or poor social skills?)
- Are they able to rate their social skills accurately?

Take a few minutes to think about the different ways you might say 'hello' to someone. Perhaps it is on the telephone, or at school; maybe it is when you come home to your family.

The greetings you use on these occasions may be different to greetings you would use when you have not seen the person for a little while.

1. Write down the name of someone that you often have to greet and say 'hello' to, and where this happens. What else do you say?

Person's name:	
Where were you:	
How do you say 'hello' and what is said afterwards?	
How successful are you at meeting and saying hello to people you see often? Circle a number below that matches your view.	

<table>
<tr><td>Very bad</td><td></td><td>OK</td><td></td><td>Very good</td></tr>
<tr><td>1</td><td>2</td><td>3</td><td>4</td><td>5</td></tr>
</table>

How do you say 'hello' to people?

2. Now think about someone you see less often – once a week, a month or even once a year. How do you say 'hello' to them? Write down your thoughts.

Person's name:	
Where were you:	
How do you say 'hello' and what is said afterwards?	

How successful are you at meeting and saying hello to people you see less often? Circle a number below that matches your view.

Very bad		**OK**		**Very good**
1	2	3	4	5

When you look at your answers for (1) and (2), is there a difference between your greetings to people you see often, and those you see less often? If so, why?

How do people chat?

This activity will help to extend the social conversation of the young person further, by identifying the strengths and weaknesses in their social responses.

In this activity, initial introductions are made for the youngster, with each social scenario dictating the type of extensions for conversation. In order for the young person to achieve here, they must have been successful in previous activities requiring social reading and correct interpretation of social scenarios.

Points to note:

- Ensure the young person can understand the context and situation; can they identify differences between the social exchanges of children and adults for instance?
- What mistakes are they making?
- Do they find it difficult to continue the conversation? What helps them?
- Are they enjoying the activity?
- Ensure that the young person ends this task feeling positive and with enthusiasm for further work in this area.

How do people chat?

In this activity you will try to think of what people might say to one another in different situations. Look at the cartoon strips and fill in the last box with what you think would be said next.

'Hello.'

'Hello. What's your name?'

'My name's Sally. What's yours?'

'My name's Jane.'

'_____
_____.'

'_____
_____.'

'Hello, Carol.'

'Hello Auntie Mary.'

'It's more than a year since I saw you last. You have grown.'

'I'm taller now.'

'_____
_____.'

'_____
_____.'

How do people chat?

'Hello Sam.'

'Have you had a good day at school?'

'_____
_____.'

'Yes thank you.'

'_____
_____.'

'Hello Karen.'

'Can you stay all day?'

'_____
_____.'

'Hello Laura.'

'Yes, I've brought lots of things in my bag for us to do.'

'_____
_____.'

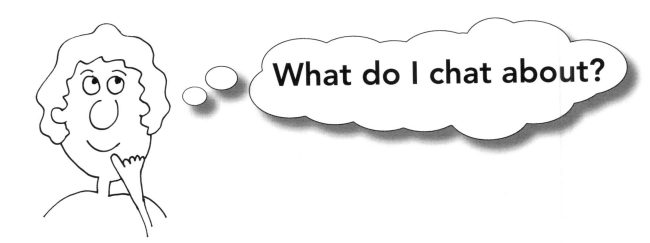

What do I chat about?

When working with a young person to develop effective communication skills it is important to ensure that they have topics about which they can freely and comfortably talk.

This exercise is simply a reflection task for the child to help them remember occasions when they were effective communicators.

Points to consider:

- Try to give the child the confidence to reflect on conversations, even if they find it difficult to bring any to mind.
- Try to offer ideas which might help the child to think back to previous conversations which have gone well.
- Who do they talk to in school / at home?
- What do they enjoy talking about?
- When do they like talking?
- What do they talk to you about?

What do I chat about?

Think of a time recently when you have had a chatty conversation. This could have been with an adult, or a child, and may have been in or outside of school.

Write down:

1. Who you were talking to

_____

2. What you were talking about

_____

3. How long you chatted for

_____

4. How did it make you feel

_____

5. Do you want to have a chat like this again

_____

Homework Ideas

Now think about some of the people you would like to chat to. Write their names here: _____

What sorts of subjects would you like to chat to them about? Write your ideas here: _____

What questions could you ask the other person when you chat?

_____

_____

Make a note of the best times and places to meet with these people and have your chats: _____

_____

Now go ahead and chat to someone, then feedback for the next exercise.

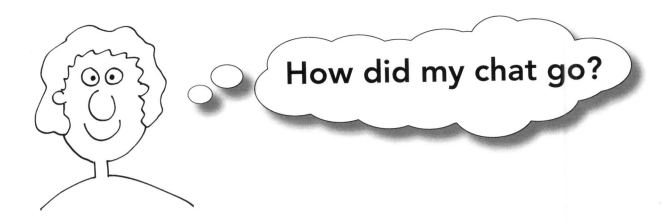

This is an opportunity to reassure the child that they have the skills to be an effective communicator. The aim is for the child to provide you with feedback on a social situation and conversation which they have structured based on the previous exercise.

Points to note:

- What are the young person's conversational strengths and weaknesses?
- Can they ask questions?
- Can they answer questions?
- Can they listen while someone else is speaking?
- Do they interrupt? Is this appropriate?
- Do they enjoy communicating?
- What helps them to enjoy communicating?

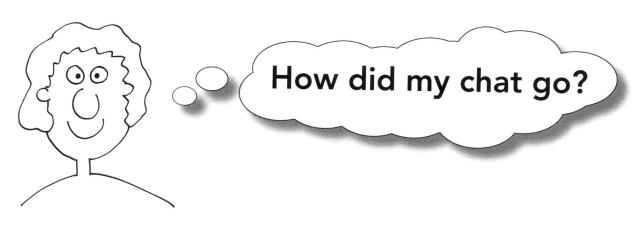

How did my chat go?

How did your chat go? Perhaps you were able to have a chat with one person, maybe you spoke to several people. It is important to think about what went well and what you could improve on.

Take a few minutes to answer as many of these questions as you can:

Who did you chat to? _____

How long did your chat last? _____

What did you talk about and what questions did you ask?

_____

What did the other person say? _____

Write down the answers they gave to your questions:

_____

_____

What questions did they ask you:

_____

_____

What would you like to chat to this person about next time?

_____

What questions do you think you might ask them?

_____

_____

How much did you enjoy your chat? Circle the number below that matches your view.

Didn't like chatting at all   **It was OK**   **Really liked chatting**
  1   2   3   4   5

What would make chatting more enjoyable for you in the future?

_____

What I do with my family at home/in a restaurant/in town

For some young people, this may be a challenging activity. They may spend very little time with their families, perhaps spending time apart in a children's home or being fostered with new families and situations. Be sensitive to each child's individual family situation and the challenges they may face in reflecting on family life.

These activities are designed to try to encourage the young person to think about everyday activities they take for granted, as well as more special family times. They may have to relate the activities to their own specific situation, reflecting on the people they spend time with outside of school, perhaps residential staff in school placements, foster parents, or care staff in residential children's homes. Equally, some youngsters may not have much time with their parents owing to separation or work patterns.

Try to negotiate these obstacles as the child will need to develop social opportunities with the significant others with whom they spend most of their time.

Before you start, you may wish to:

- Clarify with the child who is in their family.
- Clarify who is not in their family and why.
- Discuss when and where they see their family.

What I do with my family at home/in a restaurant/in town

This is an exercise to help work out what you like to do with your family!

Which places do you enjoy going to together? Are there some activities that you find more enjoyable than others? Perhaps you do these things with some members of your family, but not all of them. These are important activities as they can help develop good friendships with your family members.

Read the list of activities below and circle the ones you like doing with your family, and add some more of your own if you like.

Going to the theatre or cinema   Watching a film   Swimming

Having a meal at the dining table   Going shopping

Going out to a restaurant or a cafe   Going for a walk

Going to watching a football match   Visiting a museum

Watching a football match on TV   Playing a game

Going to a friend or relative's house for a meal   Gardening

Visiting friends or relatives   Making dinner together

Working on DIY at home   Going on holiday

Having a barbeque   Playing sports

Other things we do

_____

_____

_____

Activities with my family

As with the previous activity, it is important to use the word 'family' in its broadest sense with some youngsters. It may be helpful to think about issues the young person could face when completing these activities, including:

- Does the young person have a stable home life?
- What is their regular pattern of 'family' social activity?
- When thinking about their 'family', who do they spend most of their time with outside of school? Who cares for them? What does the child tend to do at the end of the school day, at weekends and during holidays?
- Try to establish an image of the home-life pattern that is realistic and that the child feels comfortable with.

Activities with my family

This activity will help you think about the things you are good at and enjoy doing with your family, and the things you don't like as much. Perhaps you do some of these activities with just one or two members of your family, not all of them.

Have a go at trying to finish the following sentences:

1. I like to go out for a meal with … and we usually go to …

    _____

2. At weekends I like spending time with my family doing …

    _____

3. If I had to choose a member of my family to go on holiday with it would be … because …

    _____

4. When I am at home with my family I usually talk to them about …

    _____

5. If I argue with my family it is usually about …

    _____

6. When my family and I have a meal out, we usually talk about …

    _____

7. When I am at home I prefer spending time with …

    _____

8. In my family I usually argue with …

    _____

9. If I am shopping with my parents we usually talk about …

    _____

10. The person I laugh most with in my family is …

    _____

11. The best time I have had with my family was …

    _____

What do I do with my friends?

This activity is designed to encourage young people to think about the variety of contexts in which they see their friends - at school, at home and when out together. This should prevent them from thinking about friendships in a limited sense, and encourage reflections from broader contexts.

Points to note:

- Does the young person have friendships?
- If they have few friendships, try to encourage them to think carefully about those they do have. Are there activities they don't take part in at the moment but would like to? These could be circled with a different coloured pen and used as a 'wish-list'.
- Do they have friendships that are limited to doing one or two activities together (e.g., playing computer games)? Would they like to identify some activities they might prefer to do instead?

What do I do with my friends?

What do you do with your friends? Perhaps you enjoy spending time with them at home or out at the shops. Maybe there are different things you can do with different friends.

Read the list of activities below and circle the ones you like doing with your different friends, and add some ideas of other things you might like to try.

Going to the cinema   Watching a DVD

Going out to a restaurant or cafe   Going shopping

Going to a football match   Watching a football match on TV

Going to a friends / relatives for a meal   Going for a walk

Visiting leisure centre   Visiting other friends or relatives

Cooking together   Playing games   Swimming

Gardening   Going on holiday

Having a barbeque   Playing sports

Things I would like to do with my friends

_____

_____

_____

_____

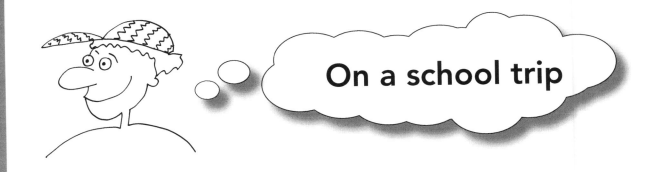

On a school trip

This is a safe activity as all young people will have been on a school trip at some time. The statements are also safe as there is no right or wrong answer – this is about the child's opinion. It will give provide an opportunity to see the youngster in a different context, one where they are structured as though in school, but are given the freedom and independence of life away from school restraints. They may therefore present as more confident, relaxed and motivated, without the encumbrances of the 'role' they may be saddled with in school.

Points to consider:

- Does the young person present with a different personality away from school?
- What is different about the child when away from school?
- How is school life affecting them?
- What do they enjoy/dislike about school? Is this affecting their behaviour in any way?
- How can the positive aspects of their behaviour away from school when on an excursion be drawn back into school life?

On a school trip

Sometimes you may behave differently while on school trips from the way you act when you are at school. Perhaps you are louder and talk more. Maybe you chat more to your friends.

Think about some of the recent school trips you have been on and then read these statements and think about whether you agree or disagree with them.

Yes / No / Don't know

1. Going on school trips is fun. _____

2. Staying at school instead of going on a trip is boring. _____

3. I talk to lots of different people on trips. _____

4. Most of my time is spent with one or two people. _____

5. On trips I can be more naughty . _____

6. Being out of the classroom is more fun. _____

7. Trips are exciting because you don't know what will happen next. _____

8. I prefer having lunch at school in the normal way. _____

9. It is nice to do different things outside of school with my friends on trips. _____

10. People are nicer when they are on school trips. _____

11. I worry about getting home when I am on a school trip. _____

12. I am fun to be with on school trips. _____

At school

This follow-on activity will further clarify the strengths and weaknesses of the child's communication around the school environment.

Points to consider:

- Does the youngster have a specific 'role' in school through which they are identified?
- How are they viewed by others?
- What type of communicators are they, and with whom?
- Are they happy at school? If not, what could help with this?

Extension Activity

This task may help create a 'communication map' for the youngster in school. To help achieve this you could:

- Ask the youngster to draw a rough map of the school.
- Using different coloured pens, shade in areas of the school to indicate how much they talk (e.g., red: talk a lot; green: talk a bit; blue: don't talk very much.)
- Write in the names of key people, activities or times of day with whom/when the youngster communicates most.

Think about the sorts of things you do with your friends at school. Do you talk to people a lot? Do you spend a lot of time on your own?

Now try to finish these sentences with your own ideas:

1. When I am at school I enjoy spending time with _____

2. Most of my lunchtime is spent _____

3. At school I like talking to _____

4. My favourite time in school is when _____

5. If I could choose who I sit next to in my lessons it would be _____ because _____

6. People at school think that I am _____

7. In school I am good at chatting about _____

8. The main reason I go to school is because _____

9. If I had to choose a favourite teacher it would be _____ because _____

10. I talk most at school when I am _____

11. If I argue with people at school it is usually because _____

12. When I leave school and go home at the end of the day I feel _____

13. When I am older and remember my time at school I will mostly think about _____

Friendships outside school

All young people need social opportunities outside of school in order for them to thrive. If a youngster struggles with this activity it is likely that they find communication very challenging and need the structure of work or school in order to be able to communicate with others.

When working on this activity, it is therefore necessary to tread carefully, encouraging all friendships and social activities outside of school to be viewed positively – no matter how small or seemingly insignificant.

If the child cannot reflect happily on events outside of school and is also not responding well inside school, it is likely that they are struggling socially and will find communication a problem.

Although poor communication skills may appear to the professional to be a problem, the child may be quite happy to have no friends or social contact and this too must be clarified.

Points to consider:

- Does the young person have much social contact outside of school?
- Is this a problem for them? If so how?
- Would the child like to have more of a social life outside of school?
- What are the roadblocks preventing this?

Friendships outside school

You may behave differently with your friends depending on where you are. For example, it may be that at school you are shy with your friends, and talk to them more outside of school.

Now read these statements and think about whether you agree or disagree with them.

Agree/Disagree/Don't know

1. My friends know and understand me better when I am outside of school. _____

2. I am more lonely at school. _____

3. At weekends I am more relaxed and good fun to be with. _____

4. I talk more to my friends at the weekends than I do at school. _____

5. I am quite unhappy at home. _____

6. I talk more when I am at school. _____

7. I don't have very many friends. _____

8. My most important friends go to school with me. _____

9. I am more shy at school. _____

10. My friends outside of school think I am really good fun to be with. _____

11. I would like more friends in school. _____

12. I would like more friends outside of school. _____

With adults

This activity tries to identify a young person's key adult relationships. This may be particularly helpful for those who have few friendships with other young people and seem to get on better with adults. The activity should also help to clarify the nature of these friendships and challenge those which may be less appropriate or beneficial.

Points to consider:

- Does the young person seem unwilling to discuss any adult relationships with you? If so – why would this be?
- Are there positive role models for the child in these adult relationships?
- Are the relationships balanced, with both adult and child benefiting from them?
- Is the young person perceiving a level of relationship which the adult might not recognise? Is this therefore a one-way friendship?
- Is the young person able to talk to adults? What are their strengths and weaknesses in communication with adults?

This activity will help you to think about how you get on with people older than you. Do you get on better with adults than children, or young people? What do you talk to adults about?

Write the names of some of the adults that you get on well with in the boxes, and note the things you talk about and do together – these could be parents or teachers, or perhaps people in charge of groups you attend.

Things we talk about are

_____

Things we do together are

_____

Things we talk about are

_____

Things we do together are

_____

Things we talk about are

_____

Things we do together are

_____

Things we talk about are

_____

Things we do together are

_____

Things we talk about are

_____

Things we do together are

_____

Things we talk about are

_____

Things we do together are

_____

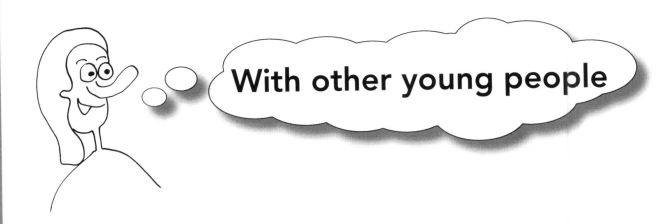

With other young people

This activity examines communication skills with other young people. It aims to clarify the nature of these relationships and what the youngster talks about and does with each person.

Points to consider:

- It may be difficult for the child to come up with five examples of relationships with other young people.
- Try to encourage thoughts about many different friendships in this age group – perhaps even cousins and extended family members.
- What strengths and weaknesses does the child present regarding their communication skills with other youngsters?

With other young people

In this activity you will think about how you get on with other children and people of your own age. Do you prefer talking to children and young people rather than adults? What do you talk about to people of your own age?

Write in the names of children or young people that you get on well with in the boxes, and note the things that you do and talk about together.

Things we talk about are

_____

Things we do together are

_____

Things we talk about are

_____

Things we do together are

_____

Things we talk about are

_____

Things we do together are

_____

Things we talk about are

_____

Things we do together are

_____

Things we talk about are

_____

Things we do together are

_____

Things we talk about are

_____

Things we do together are

_____

Do I prefer the company of other young people or adults?

Some young people will naturally prefer to communicate with adults as they are 'easier', more sophisticated, individuals who will tolerate their weaknesses, or help them to present as more skilful communicators. This is quite often the case with youngsters who have social communication difficulties.

Points to consider:

- Help the young person to identify their preferences and think about why these may be.
- Try to discover if the child has experienced bullying from others of their own age group.
- What tends to go right or wrong for the youngster when they try to communicate with adults and young people?
- What will help the young person to develop improved communication skills with adults or children?

Do I prefer the company of other young people or adults?

Looking back at the last two activities, you may have an idea about whether you prefer to talk to and do things with other children or adults. Now we need to take a closer look at who you enjoy chatting to and spending time with.

Try to answer True or False to the following statements:

True/False

1. I get on better with other people my own age than with adults. _____

2. When I am in a group of adults I have nothing to talk about. _____

3. I can only talk to adults when I am alone with them. _____

4. Other people of my own age bore me. _____

5. I can do more interesting activities with people older than me. _____

6. I prefer being in groups of people my age to groups of adults. _____

7. If I am bored I find other children more interesting to talk to. _____

8. I can only be myself if I am with people my own age. _____

9. I have nothing to talk to older adults about. _____

10. I feel the same with both older adults and people my own age. _____

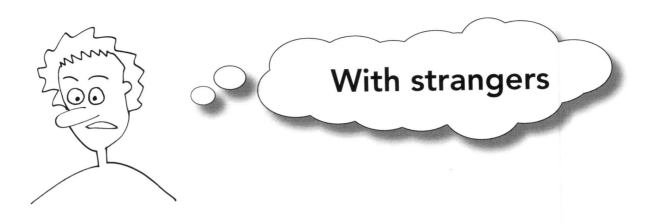

With strangers

This exercise will help to establish any inappropriate communication skills young people present in everyday interactions with people they don't know. It is helpful in this task to encourage the child to be open about their usual behaviour.

Points to consider:

- Is the young person aware of their actions and social behaviour with others?
- Are they able to reflect on the statements? Which areas are difficult for them to answer and why?
- What are the child's strengths and weaknesses when it comes to communication skills in public?
- What areas need to be targeted for further work?

Extension Activity

Try to structure a support package for the young person to become a most effective communicator in public.

- Identify the targets using this activity.
- Focus on three scenarios for development (e.g., on a bus; in a supermarket; on a high street).
- Tackle one target each week and offer feedback.
- After three weeks, re-do Worksheet 56. How does it compare? What next?

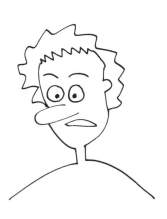

With strangers

This worksheet looks at how you get on with people you don't know – in other words 'strangers'.

Think about how you act in a supermarket, or when waiting for a bus. Do you talk to people you don't know? If someone asks you a question do you turn away from them?

Take a few minutes to read these sentences and decide how much you agree or disagree with them, and then circle the number that best fits your answer.

		Disagree		**Don't know**		**Agree**
1.	When I am in a group of people I don't know, I feel quite happy.	1	2	3	4	5
2.	If someone I don't know asks me a question, I ignore them and turn away.	1	2	3	4	5
3.	I find it easy to sit next to someone I don't know.	1	2	3	4	5
4.	I could never talk to people I don't know – even if I had to find out something important from them.	1	2	3	4	5
5.	I don't mind being around strangers, as long as I am with a good friend or someone in my family.	1	2	3	4	5
6.	It doesn't matter to me if I have to sit and talk to people I don't know.	1	2	3	4	5
7.	People I don't know are not to be trusted and I should never talk to them.	1	2	3	4	5
8.	I don't like being left on my own with people I don't know.	1	2	3	4	5
9.	It is important to talk to people and be friendly – even if you don't know them.	1	2	3	4	5
10.	You should avoid looking at people you don't know.	1	2	3	4	5
11.	I feel really worried when I am with people I don't know.	1	2	3	4	5

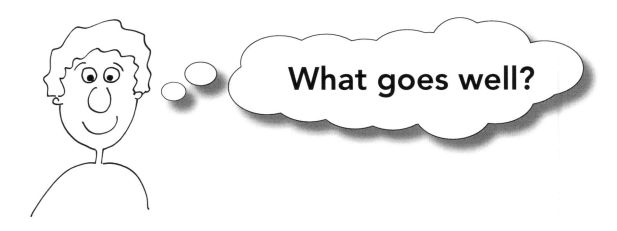

What goes well?

This is a summary sheet which will allow consolidation of information gathered in the previous tasks.

- Encourage the young person to reflect on worksheets already completed – show them the work they have done: do they see a pattern?
- What does the youngster seem to engage in most readily and with whom?
- What would be a good incentive to help the child to become a more effective communicator? This will be examined further in the Developing Skills section.

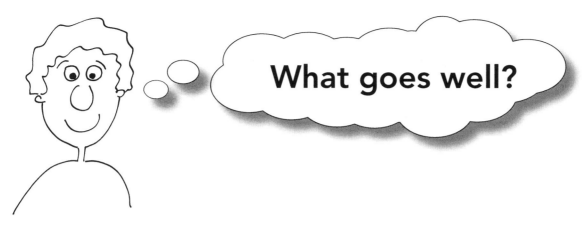

What goes well?

We have looked closely at a lot of the things you do in conversations and when chatting to other people. Now you are going to think about exactly what you are good at when talking to other people.

- Who do you like talking to most?
- What is it that you like talking about?
- Are you good at chatting to people you don't know very well?

Have a go at completing the boxes by filling in your own answers.

Remember – there is no right or wrong answer!

People I can talk to	Subjects I like to talk about
• _____	• _____
• _____	• _____
• _____	• _____
• _____	• _____
• _____	• _____
• _____	• _____
• _____	• _____

Subjects I like to listen to	People I like to listen to
• _____	• _____
• _____	• _____
• _____	• _____
• _____	• _____
• _____	• _____
• _____	• _____
• _____	• _____

What is difficult?

This task also encourages self-reflection and consolidation. Ensure the young person reviews the previous tasks, reflects on their strengths and weaknesses, and encourage them to be honest about areas of difficulty.

- Are there areas of concern for the young person?
- Are there areas of concern for the adult completing the work with the young person? Are the areas identified the same as the child's?
- What would be good targets to use as a focus?
- What would help the child?

What is difficult?

Sometimes there are things that you may find more difficult to do – perhaps talking to people you don't know very well, or talking about something you are not very interested in.

It can be helpful to know what it is that you find difficult, and the sorts of things you would like to get better at, so that you can use these as targets in the future. These are the things you want to do better so that you can feel happier!

(a) Think about the people you feel you don't get on with very well. Who are they? Write down their names.

_____

_____

(b) Now think about something you would like to be better at in conversations and when you chat to other people. Write down your ideas.

_____

_____

(c) Finally, think about the sorts of activities you would like to be better at. Look back at your worksheet 'My interests and motivations', to remind you what it is that you are good at or enjoy doing. Are there things you want to do better? Make a note of them below.

_____

_____

Now you can choose some things that you would like to work on and get better at. You need to choose a person from list (a) and something you would to be better at when you talk to other people from list (b). And finally something you want to be better at doing from list (c).

These will be some of your targets for working on next!

Section 4

Developing Skills

Developing skills

This section will help professionals working with young people to put together an action plan which will help support the child through their progression and development. It will fit equally well into Individual Education Plans (IEP) or Pastoral Support Plans (PSP). Sample target sheets and contracts are provided which can be agreed between the young person and the professional, these will help to focus on boundaries, strategies and methods for achievement.

This section of the *Toolkit* is about establishing closure through empowering the youngster to self-improve, within appropriate structures. It will also allow clarify the division of roles for each professional working around the child.

Points to consider:

- Ensure that each adult working with the young person is clear about the tasks they are assigned and the timescale for achieving these.
- Are any resources needed to ensure that the child is regularly and appropriately supported? Who else needs to be involved? How will achievements be celebrated? For how long will the support and development of skills be necessary?
- By this point in the process it will be clear where the weakest areas of communication and self-development lie. Ensure that this information is used to good effect for targeting these weak areas and use the young person's own strengths and interests as motivators for growth.

Developing skills

Now you are going to work on building on the things you can already do, and developing your achievements and abilities in the future. From your previous work you will have a good idea of what you are good at, what you enjoy and what you want to be able to do better.

The worksheets will help you to get better at things you find difficult or don't enjoy very much. They will also help you to set targets – things to aim for and get better at – and find the best way to make sure you reach your targets!

If you had to choose a skill or activity you want to improve, what would it be? Have a think, and write your answers below.

Three things I would like to be better at are:

- _____
- _____
- _____

If I had three wishes, I would wish for:

- _____
- _____
- _____

What makes me feel good

Completing this worksheet will be helped by reviewing evidence gathered from previous exercises on Worksheets 14, 15, 16 and 19. This will allow the young person to reflect on the activities they enjoy and those things they would like to spend more time doing.

Points to consider:

- Sentence completion tasks are a positive way to frame ideas – encourage the child to consider many possibilities and to 'think big' so that they are creative in their ideas.
- If they have problems finishing the sentences, you may want to revisit this exercise when they have more ideas, or have had time to think about it.
- The final box on the page asks the child to select some activities as rewards – they therefore need some good feelings around these activities. Do they need to experience some of the activities and find out whether they like them? Is this an opportunity to explore tasks and try new things? How might this be done? Who could help the child?

What makes me feel good

For this Worksheet you need to look at the ideas you have written on Worksheets 14, 15, 16 and 19 These will remind you about the interests, hobbies and activities you enjoy spending your time on. They will also tell you about the best times in your day, week and year for getting things done!

Thinking about this information, try to complete these statements, and find out what is going to help you to feel good!

1. I am most relaxed when I _____
2. My favourite sport is _____
3. I am good at hobbies such as _____
4. I really enjoy spending time _____
5. I get my school work done best when _____
6. The rewards that I work best for are _____
7. I like to collect _____
8. The thing I do best in a group or team is _____
9. I work best on my own when I am trying to _____
10. I would like to be the best at _____
11. One thing I can do well is _____
12. A new skill I would like to learn is _____
13. I could help others learn to _____
14. I always laugh and enjoy myself when _____
15. Every evening I like to spend time _____

I can therefore use the following things to help me feel good and reach my goals!

-
-

 ℗ This page may be photocopied for instructional use only. © *The Communication Toolkit*, B. Medhurst, 2009

How to make others feel good

The aim of this task is to encourage the young person to think about making socially positive responses. This will support their social development and encourage them to make new friendships, or help support those they already have.

Points to consider:

- Try to encourage the child to reflect honestly, thinking of secure skills they already possess as well as those they have the potential to develop.
- Can the youngster identify their strengths? Do they need some assistance in completing this activity? Ensure you work on this task when you know the child quite well so that you can prompt them about their achievements with other people.
- When the youngster has finished the task they need to identify some targets that they can use to help others. Ensure that these are realistic and achievable so that they have a reduced risk of failure.

This activity will look at how you help other people to feel good – what you do to help them relax and enjoy themselves more. These could be members of your family, or perhaps your friends or neighbours, or even people you only meet occasionally.

Decide if you agree or disagree with these statements and circle one of the faces. This will help you to find the things you do that make people feel happy, relaxed and good – and other things you could do in the future!

1. I am good at helping my friends with their homework. ☹ 😐 ☺
2. I like helping people when I can. ☹ 😐 ☺
3. I help out with chores at home, such as cooking or cleaning. ☹ 😐 ☺
4. Some people say I know how to cheer them up. ☹ 😐 ☺
5. If someone asks me for help, I always do my best to help them. ☹ 😐 ☺
6. On Mother's Day I do something special for my mum. ☹ 😐 ☺
7. If it is someone's birthday I try to do something they will like. ☹ 😐 ☺
8. I like to help my friends at school with their work. ☹ 😐 ☺
9. I am good at helping the teacher in class. ☹ 😐 ☺
10. I like making cards and gifts for people. ☹ 😐 ☺
11. I like helping my dad with jobs around the house. ☹ 😐 ☺
12. If someone is crying and sad I try to talk to them and make them feel better. ☹ 😐 ☺
13. When a friend is in trouble I am good at helping them out. ☹ 😐 ☺
14. When someone in my house is unwell I am good at looking after them. ☹ 😐 ☺

I can therefore use the following things to help others feel good!

-
-

This is a structured activity which will help to develop the ideas from the previous activity. Encourage the youngster to consider each scenario and think creatively about possible solutions.

Points to consider:

- Does the young person have problems thinking about solutions to these situations? If so – why?
- What are their ideas for supporting others? Do they think about tactful, supportive solutions?
- Are they able to be appropriate in their responses?
- Does the youngster need to be challenged in some of their solutions? How might you do this safely?
- Do you need to answer some of the questions as a role model for the child?

Things I can do to help people

It is always useful to have some ideas about things you can do that make people feel better. You may need to help people at home, in your family, or perhaps in school.

Try to think of things you could do in the following situations that would be helpful:

1. Someone in your family is feeling unwell and has been in bed for a few days. What can you do to help them feel better and cheer them up?
   _____

2. Someone at school is being bullied and says they have no friends. What can you do to help? _____
   _____

3. A teacher at school has hurt their leg and cannot walk far or carry things. What can you offer to do to help? _____
   _____

4. A friend of yours at school is crying and looks really upset about something. What can you do? _____
   _____

5. It is your mum's birthday and you want to do something special for her. What can you do? _____
   _____

6. You have had an argument with a friend at school and want to make it up with them. What can you do to make things better? _____
   _____

7. One of your grandparents is ill in hospital. What can you do to cheer them up? _____
   _____

How to right a wrong

This is a good activity which will help young people to think creatively around righting a wrong, using visually appealing and accessible information. It will work well with those who have difficulties in apologising, as well as those who have poor concepts of right and wrong.

Points to consider:

- Can the youngster perceive the errors in the strip cartoon story?
- If not, what is preventing them?
- Can the young person identify a solution independently? Do they need an example to model their ideas on?
- Are the solutions offered practical, real and socially acceptable?
- Does the child need to be challenged with some of their inappropriate 'solutions'? How can this be done safely?

Extension Activity

Are these real-life scenarios that are still recent or pertinent for the youngster? Do these need to be rectified?

- Ask the young person what they might be able to do or say to make things better.
- Ensure that their response is positive, helpful and 'safe' to carry out.
- Carry out a 'plan-do-review' of the response.
- Offer feedback and use the exercise to help inform future targets.

How to right a wrong

The following activities are all about trying to put things right!

Look at the cartoons and write in the boxes what you think should happen next to make someone feel better. There are no right or wrong answers – just have a go at putting things right!

How to right a wrong

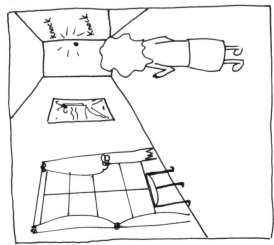

Managing my feelings

This is a helpful exercise for youngsters who are struggling to find appropriate ways of expressing their emotions. It may be that the child is angry and tends to express very negative reactions to situations. The reverse can also be true, where the child is very passive and shows little feeling or emotional response to situations requiring, for example, compassion, humour or anger.

Points to consider:

- Can the youngster use information from previous exercises to support their responses here? (Use the 'Memories and feelings' worksheet.)
- Are they answering the questions honestly? What might help them to be open?
- Does the child have difficulties expressing their emotions? If so, which emotions tend to be a problem for them?
- Can the youngster think of any memories or examples to reflect their responses here?
- What are the key concerns for the child as a result of this activity?
- Do these concerns warrant further investigation, support or management – if so, how will this be achieved?

64

Managing my feelings

Sometimes it is hard to stay in control of how you feel. Have you ever giggled at something you found really funny and not be able to stop yourself – even though you knew you might get into trouble?

Sometimes you might get very angry, or upset and tearful. It is OK to be angry and upset, and it is OK to show your emotions. But it is important that your feelings are controlled or managed, so that your behaviour does not make other people angry or upset.

What feelings do you have, and what do you do with them? Look back at the worksheet 'Memories and feelings' – what are the sorts of things you feel?

Try to finish the following sentences:

1. When someone shouts at me I tend to _____

2. If my teacher tells me off in a lesson I feel _____

3. When I feel really happy, I _____

4. If someone started a fight with me I would _____

5. People who get bullied at school feel better when they _____

6. If people turn against me and don't like me any more, I _____

7. When I get really worried or nervous I _____

8. I feel really sad about _____

9. Things that calm me down when I get angry are _____

10. I usually cry or get upset when _____

11. If I feel happy and want to laugh out loud but can't, I _____

12. The last time I got angry was when _____

13. If someone tells me to do something I don't want to do I _____

14. When I get really excited _____

Feeling in colours

Many children with social communication difficulties can 'see' their emotions more clearly in colours. They are able to match colours to emotions and use this technique to identify how they feel; furthermore they may be able to manipulate the colour to change their feeling.

As a technique this requires the youngster to reflect on a situation when they felt the emotions identified.

Points to consider:

- Help the youngster to think of times when they have experienced the different emotions listed. You could prompt if necessary.
- Can the child associate a colour with the feeling? How secure is this link?
- Can the child apply a colour to how they feel now / yesterday / when on holiday.
- Do they like to be around certain colours in the clothes they wear or in rooms.
- Can the youngster use colours to change how they feel?
- Does drawing using different colours affect how they feel?

Extension Activity
- Which colours are beneficial for the youngster?
- How can the child use these?
- When and where might they need access to these colours?
- Find a way of applying the colours in school and at home.
- Offer feedback – how has the colour change helped?

65

Feeling in colours

Some people find it easier to manage their feelings by thinking of them in colours.

For example, if you are in a bad mood, the colour of the feeling may be black. Try to work out which of the feelings you have and what colour each one would be. It might help if you have some coloured pens or pencils to write or draw with.

Feelings	Colours that match
Angry	_____
Sad	_____
Happy	_____
Scared	_____
Worried	_____
Relieved	_____
Nervous	_____
Proud	_____
Bored	_____
Embarrassed	_____
Good Mood	_____
Bad Mood	_____

Now that you have found the colours that fit your feelings, you can draw using the colours and use them to let people know how you feel.

You can use colours in your room – putting happy and relaxed colours around you to make you feel good and safe.

Try This!
You can even try swapping colours to get different feelings – for example, if you feel really 'dark green' and sad, try to think and see 'yellow' things which are happy.

Relaxing and calming down

This is a relaxation script that will need to be read through before being used with young people.

Points to note:

- Ensure that the room is warm and quiet and everyone is comfortable.
- You can use some quiet, relaxing music to help the mood. Some people use essential oils such as lavender to help relaxation, or incense sticks. Ensure that you check first that the youngster will not be irritated by this.
- Speak in a slow, low voice, unhurried and calm.
- Pause after each instruction, leaving intervals of at least 3 seconds.
- Try to take your time and don't feel self-conscious. Be confident and in control.

After the exercise the young person should be much more relaxed than when you started. They may be drowsy, but this is not a problem. If this approach works well then you could make a recording of the session that can be played back in their own time, perhaps before bedtime or when they are unwinding at the end of the day.

If the youngster finds it hard to relax with this approach, keep trying. They need to be able to relax and not feel tense or nervous. Perhaps they need to do this in the privacy of their own house and room, or may be more responsive at a different time of day.

Relaxing and calming down

Introduction

It is important that you can take it easy and relax when things get tense and you feel very upset or angry. Relaxation exercises are very good at giving you something else to do that is soothing and pleasant. They can help you feel better when you are stressed.

Note: This script needs to be read in a slow, relaxed voice, deep and unhurried. Calm music can be played in the background if possible.

I want you to think about the top of your head... I want you to think about the skin on your head and just allow it to let go and relax... now all the muscles of your face, just let them let go loose... your forehead, your eyes, your eyelids... your cheeks, mouth and jaw muscles... it's a wonderful feeling when you let your face totally relax, you can feel the skin loosening, smoothing out... let your mouth open slightly, whatever's best for you, just let it happen... relax your jaw and relax your tongue, the more you physically relax, the more your mind can relax... now think about your neck and shoulder muscles. Let them relax into the tops of your arms, letting all tensions drain away... think on down through your elbows... into your forearms... down through your wrists and into your hands... right the way down into the very tips of your fingers and tips of your thumbs... just letting all those muscles let go and relax... and now think about your breathing, noticing that you're breathing even more steadily, even more slowly, even more deeply as you relax more and more, so you can let any tension in the chest area simply drain away as you think on down to

Relaxing and calming down

your stomach muscles, letting those muscles relax, too... think down into your back now, the long muscles either side of the spine, just let those muscles relax... and your waist... and your thigh muscles, as you think on down through your knees, down through the shins and calves, just allowing all those areas to relax and let go, as you think on down through your ankles, through your feet, into the very tips of your toes... all the muscles of your body beautifully relaxed and easy... very heavy, very relaxed.

Now just breathe quietly – notice how your breathing is deeper and slower, everything feels slow and relaxed. You have nothing to worry about. Just empty your mind and let yourself drift, feeling really comfortable.

In a few minutes I am going to count backwards from ten to one. As I count backwards you will begin to feel more awake and alert and when I reach one you will open your eyes and feel refreshed and wide awake. Ready? Ten, nine, eight, your body beginning to wake up, seven, six, five, feeling more awake, your fingers and toes stretching, four, three – your legs and arms stretching, two, one, open your eyes, and gradually sit up when you feel ready. You are refreshed, relaxed, and feel wide awake.

This activity will also help young people to reflect on methods which will reduce their negative emotions. It is important that they examine all the possibilities available to them in this exercise, as there may be ways they can engage positively with activities they have never previously considered.

Points to consider:

- Ask the youngster to think about something new they could try.
- Are there three things they can go away and try that are new?
- Which methods for calming themselves down will be most effective?
- What else will be beneficial?
- How can they access the tools they need to engage in these tasks?
- Is there time in the school day that can be used? What time outside of school is available?
- Who can help the young person?

Ideas for calming down

It is important that you have a way of keeping calm and de-stressing. When you get angry or feel nervous you will feel better if there are things you can do that will make you happier.

Here are some things you can try:

Sport Exercise is good for helping you feel better. Any sport is good (team sports – football, netball, rugby or individual sports – running, swimming, ice skating or canoeing). Some more unusual activities are listed here for you to think about:

Climbing groups	Windsurfing	Martial arts
Long-distance running	Pot holing	Dance
Kick-boxing	Rowing	Skateboarding
Gymnastics	Ballet	Roller-blading

Activity Just being occupied with an activity can keep your mind off things that are worrying you or making you feel angry. These activities can be interesting and helpful:

Yoga	Pilates
Photography	Fishing
Beauty make-overs	Dress-making
Fashion design	Cooking
Woodwork	DIY
Nature watching	Art

MANAGING MY FEELINGS

Ideas for calming down

Let-the-anger-out! Sometimes you just have to let the anger out. If you are feeling really angry it can be helpful to do some of these things – try to talk to someone about doing these things before you start them:

- *Punch-bag workout.* Hitting a bag, cushion or something soft, so that you don't get hurt, can relieve your anger.
- *Screaming / shouting.* Just taking yourself to your room and screaming for one or two minutes can really let out your frustration. Put a sign on the door to explain to others what you are doing!
- *Kick a ball.* Go to a wide open space and throw or kick a ball as far as you can. It must be a safe, big space, and tell someone where you have gone or take an adult with you.

More ideas

- Talking to someone you trust.
- Keeping a diary or journal and writing it all down.
- Soft stuff or a rubber squeezy ball for holding when you feel stressed.
- Drawing or sketching.

Ideas for getting motivated

This is a task designed to motivate young people into action through focussing on specific activities which may be of interest to them. They also have the opportunity to list some of their own motivators at the end, which the task may prompt them to remember.

Points to consider:

- Are there any activities that the youngster can identify with? Are they under-motivated?
- What would encourage the child to develop motivation? Does this need structure? If so, what would it look like?
- Does the child need focus? Are they able to they choose one activity over another?
- What is likely to be the most helpful motivator for the youngster which could be used in setting goals and achieving them?
- Who would be most influential in helping the youngster to develop motivation?
- Refer back to worksheet 14 'My interests and motivations'.

Ideas for getting motivated

Sometimes you might feel fed up and miserable, or perhaps you get a bit sad, or just feel bored and need something to do.

At times like these, it is good to have something to keep you busy and stop you becoming lazy and inactive.

Look back at the things you wrote on the worksheet 'My interests and motivations'. Thinking about these ideas, put a cross in the box next the things that you enjoy doing and would find interesting – these will be your motivators!

1. Doing school work ☐
2. Having treats to work for ☐
3. Spending time with family or friends ☐
4. Computer games ☐
5. Art and craft – making things ☐
6. Reading books and magazines ☐
7. Being with animals ☐
8. Teaching others to do something ☐
9. Outdoors activities ☐
10. Physical activities or sports ☐
11. Chatting to friends ☐
12. Watching films ☐
13. Going out for the day on a trip ☐
14. Cooking ☐
15. Visiting places ☐

Are there are other things that motivate you that aren't listed.
Write them here:

_____

_____

When am I motivated the most?

In thinking about what will motivate young people, it is also important to maximise their success by considering the times of day and the different tasks that are most influential. This chart will help to focus their minds more clearly on how and when they are likely to succeed.

Points to consider:

- It is helpful if the youngster is reminded of their motivating time slots as they arise – what could help them to do this? Do they need to highlight times or dates on a calendar, set a timer or alarm, or put a note in their planner?
- How can adults support the youngster at these times?

69

When am I motivated the most?

Now that you have found the activities that motivate you, it is important to find out the times of day when you are most motivated to carry them out.

From this chart you should be able to identify what you are best at doing, and the time of day or month of the year that you feel most active.

Write your thoughts in the table below.

Tasks	Day	Month / Time of year

These will be the times you need to remember and target!

Staying in control and feeling safe

This is a simple task that will help young people to think of times and places where they feel safe and secure.

It is important that youngsters are able to identify such times and places so that if they feel unsafe, worried, angry or hurt they can easily call to mind a place where they will feel safe and relaxed.

Points to consider:

- Can the youngster access their safe place independently? Which places would be second and third best if they can't get to their first choice?
- Is there someone that the child needs to be able to access at this time? When will the person be available? What can the youngster do if they have a long wait?
- What activities does the child like to do to when they are feeling unsafe? Are any materials needed for this activity readily accessible?
- If the 'safe place' is not always achievable does the youngster have a plan B or C that they can put in place?

Extension Activity

Help the young person to draw a 'safe-map'.
- Identify the different colours that reflect when the young person feels most and least safe.
- Colour in different areas of a map of school or home according to how safe the child feels.
- Use the map to help the child to stay in their 'safe' zones.

70

Staying in control and feeling safe

This worksheet will help you to think about your safe times and places – where you can always feel relaxed and settled.

It could be that when things get busy it makes you feel a bit stressed and this might make you upset.

Thinking about your answers to these questions will help you to discover the places and activities that you can turn to if you feel upset.

1. Where do you find yourself feeling calm and relaxed? Perhaps there are several places, some indoors and some outdoors.

   _____

   _____

   _____

2. What time of day do you find it best to be in these places?

   _____

   _____

   _____

3. Are there people that you want to talk to in your safe places?

   _____

   _____

   _____

4. Are there things you like to do in these places?

   _____

   _____

   _____

Try to use your answers to these questions to plan some safe, relaxed time for yourself each day or each week.

Targets

This section will help you to focus the work done to date into a plan of action that will allow for progress to be measured.

Points to consider when setting targets:

- The young person should have ownership of the targets – they should feel a degree of autonomy and control over their selection and development.
- It is important that the contracts are not seen as a method of controlling the child. The intention is that they help the young person to develop their emotional self-regulation.
- Some young people respond very well to the support, recognition, structure and attention that comes with the use of a contract.
- Other young people will feel under pressure when contracts are used. For these youngsters, a flexible approach is necessary that encourages ownership.
- Which people need to be involved in setting targets, plans and contracts?
- What is likely to support a most positive outcome?

71

Target planner

Now you are going to look back on the worksheets you have completed and think about the areas that need some more work. These will form the targets that you need to aim for in the future.

Targets can be big or small – the smaller ones are just as important as the big things as they are often harder to achieve.

Fill out the boxes below by following steps 1–3:

1. Look back at the worksheets you have worked on and find them in the list below.
2. Check which activities you have completed in these sections and put a cross in the 'Completed' box for each one.
3. Now think about areas where it would help you to do further work and put a cross in the box 'More work needed'. These will be some of your targets!

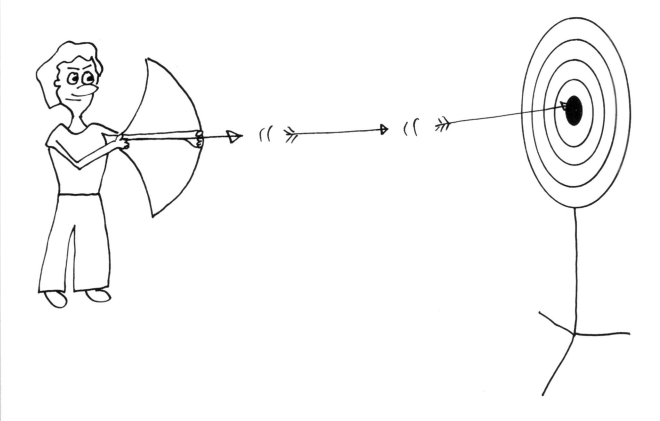

Target planner

	Completed	More work needed

Social-Emotional

1. Self-Esteem: making myself feel better about me
   Worksheets 11–16, 19–20, 24, 60, 64–70 ☐ ☐
   making others feel better about me
   Worksheets 22, 23, 61–64 ☐ ☐

2. Friendships: developing stronger friendships in the family
   Worksheets 1–9, 47–48 ☐ ☐
   developing stronger friendships with friends
   Worksheets 17–18, 22, 49–54 ☐ ☐

3. Understanding emotions
   Worksheets 10–13, 21, 41–42, 64–70 ☐ ☐

4. Understanding body language
   Worksheets 28–30, 36–39 ☐ ☐

5. Understanding how to communicate
   Worksheets 25–27, 31–35, 40–46, 55–59 ☐ ☐

Social Communication

1. Greetings and saying 'hello' (Worksheets 26, 43) ☐ ☐
2. Chatting and talking to people I know (Worksheet 44) ☐ ☐
   to strangers (Worksheet 56) ☐ ☐
3. Reading 'body language' (Worksheets 28–29) ☐ ☐
4. Reading a social picture (Worksheet 33) ☐ ☐
5. Predicting how someone feels (Worksheet 37) ☐ ☐
6. Predicting what will happen next (Worksheet 38) ☐ ☐
7. Making a mistake (Worksheet 40) ☐ ☐
8. Trust (Worksheet 41) ☐ ☐
9. Other things I find difficult (Worksheet 58) ☐ ☐

2 of 2

Target sheets

Here are some examples of target sheets, contracts and memory joggers that you can keep or pin up in different places to remind you of the things that you have to work on, and the ideas that are going to help you!

These are only examples – you can use them or make up your own and put your own pictures and designs on them if you like – whatever helps you stick to the plan!

These are going to be your keys to success so be careful about what you choose to be your targets.

Remember – targets must be **SMART**:

Small/Specific

Measurable

Achievable

Realistic

Timely

Ask someone to help you work on these!

My targets!

Things I will achieve by:

_____

(Date)

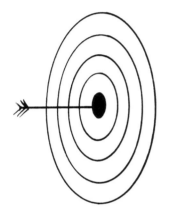 **Target 1:**

_____

_____

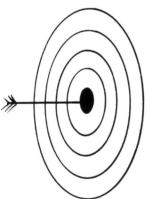 **Target 2:**

_____

_____

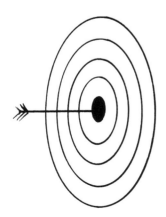 **Target 3:**

_____

_____

DEVELOPING SKILLS

My contract

I want to achieve the following targets:

1. _____

2. _____

3. _____

In order to achieve the above targets I will need these people to help me:

_____ will help me with

_____

_____ will help me with

_____

Rewards that will help me to work towards my targets:

TARGETS

• _____

• _____

• _____

I agree that I will do all I can to achieve these targets and will review my progress on: _____ (date)

Signed: _____

Supported by: _____ (staff)

Supported by: _____ (parent)

My memory jogger

Things I need to remember!

Date	Remember

Things I tend to forget!

- _____
- _____
- _____
- _____
- _____
- _____

DEVELOPING SKILLS

My motivator reminders!

Sometimes you can forget the good things – you need to remember how important and good you really are!

Things to feel good about!

I am good at: _____

I have achieved: _____

People like me because I: _____

My friends are: _____

I am looking forward to: _____

My 'motto' is: _____

TARGETS

Things which help to motivate me when I feel tired, unwell, unhappy or angry are:

- _____
- _____
- _____
- _____

Chill Out!

I must take care of myself
and relax when I feel stressed.

The things that help me are:

- _____
- _____
- _____
- _____
- _____
- _____

Toolkit

The worksheets in this section are some strategies that young people may find useful in building their 'Toolkit'.

Read through these worksheets with the youngster and explore which of the strategies would be most beneficial.

- Try to encourage the young person to think positively but realistically about the tools; some may really help them but others may carry a risk of failure. For example joining a group before they are ready to do so may make them feel incompetent or uncomfortable.

- Ensure that a support network is in place around the youngster when they tackle something new, so that they have someone to talk to and debrief them afterwards. The child may need someone to accompany them when they tackle new activities and to reflect their observations as a 'reality check'.

- Ask the youngster to identify the methods of support raised in this section that they find appealing.

- Try to be creative with new activities and methods of support for the child. For example, is a mood thermometer a good idea? Would the youngster benefit from games which develop their memories about life events? Are comic strips helpful in developing social awareness?

- Think about the supporting role of the adults around the child; who will need to do what?

When you have a job to do, you need to find the right tools to help!

Now you have found out which areas you need to target, it will help if you know the best ways to reach your goals!

What Helps Me

You might already have some ideas of the sorts of things that will help you to reach your targets. Perhaps you will work harder in some lessons, or try to talk more to your friends – these are all good ideas!

It can be useful to have a few other ideas to use to make sure you reach your goals - some of these may help:

Comic Strip Cartoons

It can be difficult to try to tell someone how you feel about something that has happened. It might be easier to draw what happened using stick cartoons, like this:

By using a stick cartoon it doesn't matter if you can't draw! And you can put in speech or thought bubbles to let people know what you said and what you thought.

TOOLKIT

You may want to use some of the ideas in the picture above to make your cartoons more exciting!

Toolkit

Have a go at drawing your own cartoon, using something that was said to you or that happened to you recently.

Toolkit

Scripts

If you need to remind yourself of something, it is helpful to write it down. Sometimes you might forget what to do or say to people, or you might forget to remind yourself about something – like how brilliant you are!

Writing a script can help you. Write down in short sentences the things you need to remember. Keep the sentences positive, such as:

I am good at _____

I will be _____

I have really good _____

It will help if I _____

People like me to _____

It is important to _____
I am really important!

Keep the script to one side of paper and make sure it is easy for you to read. When you have written down the things you want to remember, make several copies of your script, and stick them in places where you will read them (e.g., on your bedroom wall, on the fridge door, in your school log-book, on the back of the toilet door!).

Have a go at writing a script – write a few sentences about some good things that you should remember about yourself and others.

Toolkit

My Script

I must read this every day and remember these important things to help me!

- _____
- _____
- _____
- _____

I should remember these things – I am a good person!

Join a group!

Think about joining a club or group that meets regularly. Here are some ideas:

Cubs / Scouts / Guides / Youth group /Church group / Choir / Musical Band / Theatre Group / Sports Group / Voluntary organisations or charities / Environmental groups – World Wildlife Fund for Nature (WWF) or Royal Society for Protection of Birds (RSPB) / Gardening club Or you could start your own! Do you have a school council? Perhaps you want to support recycling in your school, or help run the school fete.

Perhaps you want to start your own band in school! Or you could start a school magazine or debating society.

TOOLKIT

Measure the feeling – Thermometer

Trying to measure your feelings can be helpful. Although you might think you feel very angry, measuring how strongly you really feel can help you recognise your emotions and can be the first step towards calming them down.

Have a go now! Look at the thermometer, and mark off where you feel right now:

You might want to mark a time when you think you last felt really angry, and when you felt really relaxed – this will help you to work out how strongly you feel about something.

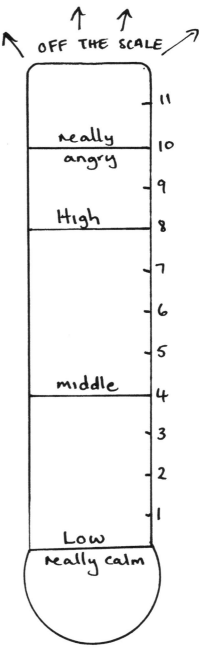

OFF THE SCALE

11
really angry 10
9
High 8
7
6
5
middle 4
3
2
1
Low
really calm

Toolkit

Try This!

Here are some blank thermometers so you can label and measure your own feelings – perhaps you want a sad-happy thermometer, or a worried–relaxed thermometer.

Put them where you will see and use them.

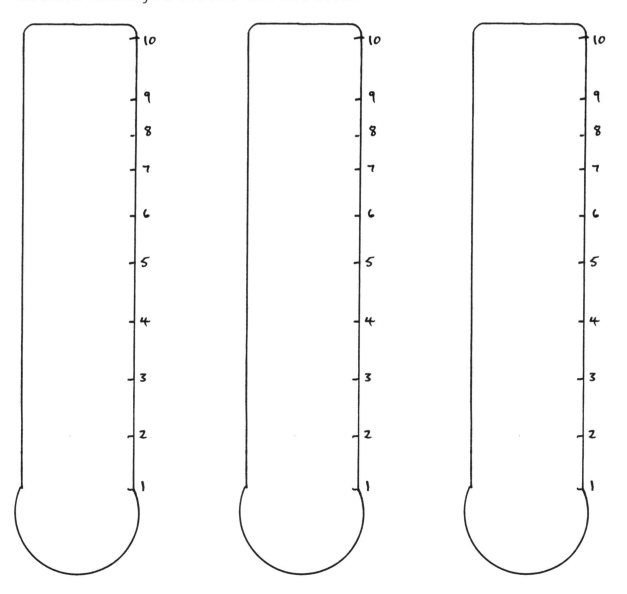

Rewards

It will help you to reach your targets if you know you'll get a reward once you get there!

Rewards are the things you enjoy – they can be things you like to eat, play with, spend time doing or be given. You will already know some of the things that could be rewards from worksheets 14, 24 and 60.

Other rewards might include:

- Spending special time with your mum or dad.
- Decorating your bedroom.
- Buying some new clothes.
- Having piano or horse-riding lessons.
- Getting sponsorship for your favourite charity.

Use some of these ideas and the ones from the worksheets to help you fill in this targets and rewards chart – remember you can pick other rewards that might help you!

Target	Date due	Reward

People who will help me

Members of your family, friends or people at your school or clubs can help you to reach your targets and goals.

You might need different people for different targets – for example, a teacher can help you get better at keeping calm in the classroom, but you might want a friend to help you meet new people outside of school.

You should talk to the person whose help you want, so that you can get their agreement to you putting their name on the target sheet. You also need to think about how they can help you. What is it you want them to do? And when do you want them to do it?

Write your ideas in the chart, thinking about who you want to help with each target. It's OK to use the same person more than once, if you think they are the best one for the job!

Target	By when	Reward	Person to help

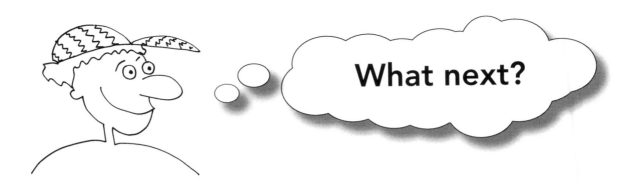

What next?

If further activities are needed for a youngster's development they should be apparent at this point. The conclusion of this programme is an opportunity for closure with the young person, encouraging them to develop further independently or setting ways forward for the future.

If a young person has further issues that are still largely unresolved, this is the time to be thinking about where to go next. You may have discovered clear gaps in the child's skills and knowledge that need more work. Alternatively, the youngster may have made as much progress as they are able to at this time, and a break from the programme is now needed.

Closure is always a challenge when working with young people, especially if the work to date has been supportive and helpful in the youngster's growth. Try to use this time to celebrate progress and remind the youngster of how far they have come. Finally, use the time to signpost them to future.

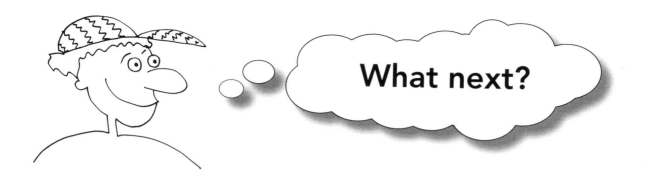

What next?

You will now have an idea about what you are good at and what you need to work on. You should also have some good ideas about targets you can work towards and the best ways to reach them, with help from rewards, strategies and people.

You may find that reaching your goals is more difficult than you think. You may need to look again at some of your worksheets, perhaps completing some questions and activities more than once. You might get different results on different days!

Don't be afraid to:
- Try the activities more than once.
- Complete different sets of targets at different times.
- Ask for more help from different people.

Perhaps you need more support, or to do a bit more work on one of the areas we have looked at.

There are lots of different things that will help you – including:
- Comic strip cartoons
- Counselling and therapies
- Social stories

Don't be afraid to ask for help – and find out what support is available and how it can help you. If you have trouble asking for help, there are some 'Help' cards in this Toolkit, which you can hand to people – write on them the things that you need help with.

**And remember – you are a good person and can reach your targets!
Keep going!**

DEVELOPING SKILLS

WHAT NEXT?

What next?

Bibliography

Burns, D., 1999, *The Feeling Good Handbook*, Penguin Books Ltd.

Gray, C., 1994, *Comic Strip Conversations – Illustrated interactions that teach conversation skills to children with autism and related disorders*, Future Horizons.

Gray, C., 2000, *New Social Story Book*, 2nd edition, Future Horizons.

Jordan, R., 1991, *Therapeutic approaches to autism*, National Autistic Society Conference Proceedings, 3–6 April, University of Durham.

Smith, C., 2003, *Writing and Developing Social Stories – Practical interventions in Autism*, Speechmark Publishing Ltd.

Willson, R. & Branch, R., 2006, *Cognitive Behavioural Therapy for Dummies*, John Wiley.

Wing, L.,1996, *The Autistic Spectrum*, Constable.

Have you seen ...

3 Minute Motivators

More Than 120 Activities to Help you Reach, Teach and Achieve!

Kathy Paterson

This resource will show you how to turn around unmotivated, unfocused classes. With more than 120 practical and simple ideas that will refocus a group, release excess energy, or start a class with a bang.

Offering a wide variety of ready-to-use activities that turn potential problems into opportunities, and get pupils out of a rut and into a more productive mode:

- *Calm Down* – relaxing activities that let imaginations soar
- *Get Moving* – lively motivators
- *Act, Don't Speak* – silent but fun activities
- *Words and Movement* – activities that mix talk with action
- *Single Words & Sounds* – simple communication activities
- *Conversation* – getting motivated one-on-one
- *Brainstorms* – working together to let the ideas fly
- *Paper & pencil activities* – from letter and word play to shared stories.

An ideal resource for all teachers, teaching assistants and those running groups, promoting playful activities that involve competition, cooperation and opportunities to focus on real learning.

2009 • 168pp • A4 paperback • ISBN 978-1-906531-00-3

Hinton House Publishers Ltd
Newman House, 4 High Street, Buckingham, MK18 1NT, UK
info@hintonpublishers.com
www.hintonpublishers.com